What a charmer! This guy obviously liked to give his audience ~~migraine~~ headaches, judging by his ~~taste~~ in clothes. The daisies on his ~~tasteful~~ "bolero" waistcoat were undoubtedly sewn on by his mother, as this family certainly like to look after each other. Nowadays this young man is a touch more retiring, almost to the point of being a recluse. He's grown up a lot since this shot was taken, though, and so he could probably donate this delicious outfit to his friend and mentor, Bubbles the chimpanzee (!). Alternatively he could always give those shirt collars to the local hang-gliding club.

5. That perm, those socks, that shirt! Worraman! The whole BJ gang have gone wildly passionate (bloag!) over this swoonsome photo of one of today's "very big megastars". How could he possibly bear to stay in the public eye after walking the pavements of Britain in those vinyl moccasins? What's worse, his tinfoil gloves are perched on the table just waiting to get put on. Delicious! This man was certainly a true fashion victim. This is actually a rather 'sensible' shot of him at this point in his career. It wasn't unknown for him to dress up (a might too convincingly, we should add) as a woman and also in Pierrot-type knicker-bockers and pointy hats! (Ooer!)

6. Well, wouldn't you hide in the nearest bush if you had togs like this on? Pity we can't see his yesteryear popster's trousers as it's a dead cert that they're horrifically ginormous flares. And what about those tasteless jacket lapels that just seem to scream out "Make me smaller! Make me smaller!" If you were back in the early 70's this guy would be very likely your number one mega-hunk. Aren't you glad you were born too late, ha! ha!?

7. Crivvens, what perfect frights!

Obviously the bloke at the front had just been watching 'The Sound Of Music' and decided to run up a little "number" out of his parlour curtains. He's obviously the black sheep of this family, as his two brothers are cringeing wildly behind him. As for the sensible one at the front, well, he must have been so mortified at all the fashion malarky around him that he promptly left the band! Can you blame him?

The other three mystery men have been successful through the 70's and made yet another comeback in 1987. So who are they then?

8. Forget the gruesome fashion failures of the pop world. What about the stars whose hairdressers obviously have some massive grudge against them? This guy should sue! Rather surprisingly, his career wasn't ruined because of this "coiffure".

This guy broke up with two other musical friends in the early 80's but continued his musical career with some rather more soulful toons. He married his backing singer last year, so hopefully she'll not file for divorce when she catches sight of this spooky haircut!

9. Is this the the man of your dreams, or what? Back in the 60's (and yes, even today) fanatical females everywhere throw their undergarments on stage when he does his "act". He's got a penchant for bedecking himself with awfully big 'trinkets' such as the ten ton bracelet and teensy weensy signet ring he's sporting here. As for the tie, it looks like his mother knitted it for him! Yessiree, the original medallion man, and no doubt about it!

10. This precocious young miss is pictured here on her first fashion shoot when she was 17. These days she often wears, um, a lot less clothes and even manages to make a living from it! Recently she's also "branched" into singing and her career has fairly "blossomed" since! Nothing's gonna stop her now, or so she says. Well, after you lot have seen her in this gorgeous Terry-towelling shorts set she might see her record sales plummet, har de har har!

CONTENTS

4

UPFRO

BRUSH STROKES

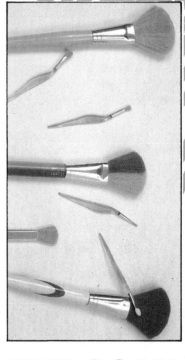

As many a self-respecting beauty knows, the only way to achieve a professional-looking make-up is by using make-up brushes like the professionals themselves use!

The great big fluffy ones are for dusting on a fine layer of powder which goes on after the ol' foundation. Then there are the smaller fluffy ones for blusher and the teeny-weeny brushes for applying and blending eyeshadow, eyeliner and lipstick. Intellectual stuff, eh, gals!

Anyway, here's a few choice specimens to spend your pennies on . . .
Pink/green powder brush, £2.99. From Top Shop.
Small pink brush set, £2.99. From Top Shop.
Orange/yellow powder brush, £3.50. From Boots.
Pink/purple brush, £3.99. From Zig Zag.

THE COMIC STRIP

Wear your sense of humour on your chest with these wacky T-shirts!

Mickey Mouse "James Dean" T-shirt, Miss Piggy "True Blonde" T-shirt, both from Top Man. Hyyyaaahh!!

Where Did You Get That Hat?

"If you want to get ahead, get a hat," so they say! Hats are indeed a girl's best friend — a real fashion essential!

Not only can they hide that "perm that went wrong" or that "boyish crop that left you looking more like a skinhead than Twiggy", but they can also jazz up an otherwise boring outfit. Yes indeedy, readers, hats are well and truly HIP!

Famous folk who swear by their hats:
Ben — Curiosity
Abraham Lincoln
Alannah Currie
Boy George
Mick Jones
Chris Lowe
Queen Mum
Gertrude Schilling

CHRISTMAS SONGS

1. "Lonely This Christmas" — Mudd
2. "I Saw Mommy Kissing Santa Claus" — Beverley Sisters
3. "Merry Xmas Everybody" — Slade
4. "Happy Xmas (War Is Over)" — John Lennon
5. "Blue Christmas" — Elvis
6. "Little St. Nick" — Beach Boys
7. "Another Rock 'n' Roll Christmas" — Roy Wood
8. "Wombling Merry Christmas" — The Wombles
9. "I Wish It Could Be Christmas Everyday" — Roy Wood & Wizzard
10. "Last Christmas" — Wham!

Scooby Doo T-shirt, from Virgin.
Flintstones T-shirt, from Top Man. OK, Barney!

Garfield T-shirt from Millets.

UPFRONT

Oh woe is me! Alas, for legs like this. Long and stick-like, they're the legs of a foxter to be sure. Makes a girlie all the more determined to stick to her diet, take more exercise and ne'er touch even a square of choco ever again . . . pass the carrots, puh-lease.

6

WHAT UPFRONT WOULD LIKE TO FIND IN ITS STOCKING:

1. Billy Bragg, Mickey Rourke, Zody, Sir Billiam of Idol or any combination of the four
2. Many a glittering gem
3. Jaffa cakes
4. Peanut butter (crunchy, naturellement)
5. Chocolate Money (who says we only think of food? ahem . . .)
6. Dosh a-plenty
7. Long, elegant, THIN legs
8. A white peroxide crop that suits us
9. Milky Bar Buttons (mmmmmm)
10. Terence Trent D'Arby's phone number

Pooh Bear reversible sweatshirt, from Top Shop.

Jeffrey Rogers "Three's Company" T-shirt, "On Shore Leave" T-shirt, both from Wrygges.

Shots from Cleveland College of Art and Design in Hartlepool, and Newcastle Polytechnic.

● Yuss indeedy, how would today's modern missy be without many a funky garment on her bod? Pretty cold, that's how! Haw haw haw... But seriously, gals, take a trendee peek at what today's bright sparks have got planned for the fashion peaks of tomorrow...

7

CHRISTMAS
FOOD

1. **Mince Pies**
2. **Christmas Pudding**
3. **Brandy Butter**
4. **Turkey**
5. **Selection Boxes**
6. **Quality Street Chocs**
7. **Tangerines**
8. **Chocolate Money**
9. **Sherry Trifle**
10. **Chocolate Novelties**
    off the tree

Daffy Duck "Play It Cool" T-shirt, from Top Man.

Thunderbirds Lady Penelope T-shirt, from Top Man.

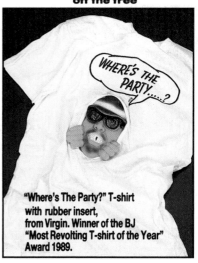

"Where's The Party?" T-shirt with rubber insert, from Virgin. Winner of the BJ "Most Revolting T-shirt of the Year" Award 1989.

HAIR TODAY, GREEN TOMORROW?

If your barnet's in need of a tonic, then there's no better way to do it than to use one of them thar conditioning hair colourants. We got a few of the BJ gang in the bathroom and poured some gunge on their bonces — with varying results . . . !

NIKKI: Harmony "Honey Hazel" Hair Colour.

"I really liked this — in fact, several washes after, I still do! It's lasted pretty well, though it's a wee bit faded. It didn't dry my hair out, either, as permanent dyes tend to: in fact, it left my hair really shiny. Added to that, it's very reasonably priced — worra winner, 10 out of 10!"

JACQUIE: Colour Glints "Raisin" Hair Colour Cosmetic.

"Blah! This was rubbish! First of all, the instructions were unclear — it didn't say whether you should just apply it to damp hair or actually shampoo your hair first. Then I thought it'd be less messy since it was in a tube rather than a sachet. Nosiree, it got everywhere, especially the bathroom walls! And after all that, did it make the teensiest bit of difference? Did it nick! A waste of time — a big fat zero out of 10."

LESLEY: Toners "Auburn Glow".

"I've got very dark hair anyway, so it didn't really alter the colour of my hair at all. However some people did comment that my hair had sort of reddish tints to it. But it's pretty messy to use and the instructions on the back were covered with purple gunge — not to mention the bathroom! Overall verdict? Good for bringing out the highlights in your hair, but don't expect a transformation — 6 out of 10."

MORAG: Shaders "Silver Frost".

"When it comes to hair dyes, my bonce has seen it all. I've used more dye than I've had hot dinners, and consider myself to be a veritable expert on the subject. Whether it's because my hair's been so saturated with other dyes or not, this stuff made scarcely a hint of a change to my colour, which (right now) is a pearly blonde colour anyway. If anything, it got a little darker rather than gaining silvery highlights as it was supposed to. Sorry, but I wasn't impressed — 2 out of 10."

ALI: Paletta Affairs "Chateau Burgundy" Hair Colouring Creme.

"This was a bit of a no-no for me. The instructions said 'leave on for 10-30 minutes' and as my hair is quite dark and doesn't take colour very well, I left it on for 25 minutes. Was there any difference? None whatsoever, it must be said. Still, I don't want to be too hard on it as very few dyes make a difference to my hair. 5½ out of 10."

And what was the general verdict?

"This kind of stuff's great to try and bring out your own natural colour, but don't go looking for drastic changes."

Silver/black and gold/black spotty hairbows, £1.50 each. From Top Shop.

Gold/silver/bronze bangle from a selection at Zig Zag, Dundee.

Gold/black and silver/black spotty bandeaux, £2.99 each. From Top Shop.

HEAVY METAL

Take a plain, boring outfit, add one or more of these dead trendy accessories and shine . . . ! !

Large leopard brooch, £2.99; small leopard, £6.99. Both from Top Shop.

Selection of Ultra Colour make-up available from Boots.

● Fed up with your hair, girlies? Bored with seeing the same ol' barnet but every day? What you need is something fairly versatile, yah? Well, we've picked out a selection of styles, all of which are easy to keep, but you can do lots of different things with . . .

1. This classic bob has the front and sides razored thin to create a wispy effect. Wear it pinned up of a funky evening out or tied back with the fringe left spikey for a simpler look.
   Hair by Alan Paul Hairdressing.

2. For long-haired girlies . . .
   Fine sections of hair are twisted together with wax, then some of the tendrills are twisted together on the top of the head to achieve this dreamy look.
   Hair by Level.

3. Ooer! These brilliant curls were created with a 'Drop Twist Perm'. This involves a special winding technique which produces this natural look. Alternatively, it can be scrunched tightly at the bottom to give the impression of the whole style shrinking. A winner, eh?
   Hair by Level.

4. Another one for long-haired chicks. Long hair is layered throughout and swept up on top for a sophisticated look. For a more casual look, leave the hair down and brush forward.
   Hair by Alan Paul.

   Alternatively, you can pin the hair as in this shot, leaving a few front layers loose, which helps retain softness around the face.
   Hair by Level.

5. A shorter style this one. Hair is cut into a one length bob shape with the fringe left just skimming the eyebrows.
   Hair by Level.

UPFRONT

ALL JUMBLED UP

Spook! It's been discovered that the Blue Jeans staff like nothing better than a jolly old scrum for bargains at the local jumble sales and junk shops. (Could this be a reflection on our wages?! — Very broke BJ gang.) So if you're sitting comfortably we'll tell you about our wondrous bargains (most of which have been shoved to the back of the wardrobe by now!).

GAYLE, THE ED

It's difficult to know where to begin — you see I buy 99% of my clothes second hand. My best bargains ever in the whole wide world and Africa would have to be my Chelsea boots (50p), my black denim jacket (£1), my Victorian frock coat (£2) and my Harris Tweed suit (£10). Buying second hand means that no one can copy you exactly. (Ha! Who'd want to? — The BJ gang.)

FIONA

I'm not one to frequent junk shops, and if I do I usually say "Golly gosh — that's a bargain!", pay my 40p or whatever and end up never wearing it. However, I do like really horrible tasteless kipper ties from the 70's. (We've noticed! — Cringing BJ gang.) I also once bought an antique, fully operational sewing machine for a fiver. The corkscrew in the picture comes in very useful for opening ginger beer (oh aye, and what else?). I got it at a flea market in Portugal for about 30p. It's dead gaudy and tasteless but is v. close to my heart. (Mm quite, Fiona.)

MARLYN

My best buy (although I don't think they were really a "bargain") were my flying seagulls (yes, seagulls). They're a set of two and they're quite large and very much at home flying across my living-room wall. (Em, how "tasteful", Marlyn (!).) They cost £6, and were worth it for the novelty value because everyone has flying ducks, don't they? Well, Hilda Ogden did . . .

NIKKI

I bought a really groovy coffee set from the Muscular Dystrophy shop in Aberdeen. It's really cute — white with a blue flowery pattern all over, but the best bit is that the saucers are black. Anyway, it cost £5 and is the nicest set of junk in the world!

LESLEY

One of my many bargains was an old-fashioned filing cabinet I bought at a market stall for £11. Dead good for stuffing all my "accoutrements" in and worra snip to boot! This red hunting jacket cost about a tenner in Flip and is the snuggliest warmest item of clothing I own. The badge was from Flip too and adds a certain touch of "je ne sais quoi" dontcha think? (No — The Ed.) I can skip through the office pretending I'm Little Red Hiding Hood when I'm wearing this, so it's got good chuckle value too. (Pardon? — Mystified BJ gang.)

MORAG

Well, I'm a sucker for second-hand shops and usually buy things only to regret it an instant later. Amongst things now banished to the cupboard are a fur coat (£5) and a 30's cocktail dress. Despite the contrary evidence in this photo, I have bought some tasteful things in my time, such as an old-fashioned set of combinations (all woolly and comfy) and a brown leather briefcase I use as a "handbag" — I got that for £8 and it's a bashed but much-loved accessory. This dog was found in a shop in Edinburgh for 10p and as you can probably tell I'm quite into tasteless objects. I keep hoping I'll see it on the Antiques Roadshow valued at squillions of pounds then I can retire and live in the Bahamas . . . is that enough? Oh, but then there was the . . . (Morag toddles off into the sunset blabbering on about her wondrous "snips".)

10

10 Resolutions Girlies Always Make

1. Become a stick through dieting.
2. Take more exercise.
3. Stop biting nails.
4. Keep bedroom tidy.
5. Have hair cut regularly.
6. Clean teeth twice a day.
7. Do homework on time.
8. Stop being shy.
9. Experiment with make-up.
10. Become a style warrior.

CHRISTMAS PURSUITS

1. Sending a letter up the chimney to Santa (Whaddya mean, you grew out of that when you were 7??)
2. Watching the Queen's speech
3. Fighting about which channel to watch on TV
4. Eating chocolate for breakfast
5. Eating turkey and trimmings till you're full enough to burst
6. Eating chocolate in the afternoon
7. Pulling crackers and wearing silly paper hats
8. Playing board games and falling out with Dad/Mum/little brother/big sister
9. Playing Phil Spector's album of Christmas hits
10. Eating chocolate before you go to bed

SHAPE UP FOR SPRING

● OK, turn out your pockets, bin those Wispas (or, um, you could post them to Upfront, if you'd prefer) and let's start the year with a healthy eating campaign. There's no need to go crazy and starve yourself, just cut down on nastee stodge such as cakes, biscuits, sweets, jam, chips and white bread. We didn't say cut them out, just go easy! Eat loads of fresh fruit and veg, brown bread and lean meat, and switch to low-fat spreads and skimmed milk. The yukky flab'll fall away, especially if you follow suggestion number two . . .

● Work that body! Yup, make your square-eyed days in front of the TV a thing of the past and take up some form of exercise. Aerobics, tennis, badminton, swimming, jogging — even walking'll help. If it all sounds a bit tiring, you'll be surprised how much more energy you have left. You'll still be able to boogie on down at the local hot spot, have no fear . . .

● It's not much use having a slim and foxlicious body if you have to wear mittens to hide your disgusting, split and chewed nails. Give yourself a manicure every week. UPFRONT's told you how, so get going!

● Give yourself a facial. Steam out those nasty blackheads — put your head over a basin of boiling water, put a towel over your head, and it'll really open your pores. Gently squeeze the yukky things out, then follow with a mild cleanser, toner and moisturiser. Voilà! Perfect skin . . .

● Get your hair cut, and resolve to get it trimmed every few weeks from now on. Zap it up with a temporary colour if you fancy a change — there are dyes a-plenty to choose from. (See our wondrous wee feature.)

RESOLUTION BLUES

I was determined to go out with Scott Taylor – whether he liked it or not!

Short Story by Jim Ward

"**Y**OU'LL never do it," said Paula. "You haven't got the willpower."

She was right, of course, but you know what it's like with New Year's resolutions. Who wants to see how often you can sleep in late, or how many Mars bars you can demolish in ten minutes? It's much more fun tormenting yourself with trying to be more helpful at home, giving up sugar in your tea, and doing your homework on time. No wonder the good intentions never last beyond the week.

Take last January, for example. I had this crazy idea of giving up chocolate. Not to mention getting Scott Taylor to ask me out. Scott was this fab-looking boy in my class. Not that he'd ever noticed me. But I was going to change all that. I'd been studying him — checking out the sort of girls he dated — which was just about everyone except me, so far as I could see.

OK, so I've got this problem with puppy fat. But how come everyone goes mad over puppies and not over me? There's no justice in the world!

Paula reckoned I was wasting my time. She's my best friend, though you wouldn't think it, sometimes. I told Paula that I was going to go out with him whether he liked it or not. She said she expected he wouldn't like it very much and that was when I nearly clobbered her with my bag. Well, a girl can go too far — and I sometimes wished she would. Australia might have been far enough, I reckoned, but she didn't seem to get the joke.

You see, there were some people who reckoned that all Scott Taylor cared about was himself. One girl he went out with said he spent longer in front of the mirror plucking his eyebrows than she did, but that was probably sour grapes because he ditched her for the girl who works in the beauty shop at weekends. And anyway, even if it was true, a girl can learn from her mistakes, can't she? And I reckoned Scott Taylor was a pretty good mistake to learn from. If only I could get him to go out with me at least once. I mean, he didn't know what he was missing! He's better off not knowing, said Paula, which I reckoned was pretty bitchy even by her standards.

That's when I decided to fall back on Dave. Dave was my next-best friend and great fun, too. But he was what you might call one of life's runners-up. He was the sort of boy who always did brilliantly in the exams but never came higher than second place; the guy who was way ahead of most people in the queue, but still managed to be the first one not to get chips with his peas because they'd just run out.

He was first substitute in the school football team — and hadn't played a game all season because no one was off-form or ill. That was Dave's luck for you.

It was a rotten shame too, because he was one of the nicest guys around. I couldn't understand why he'd never had a girlfriend, but that was his business, I suppose. Anyhow, the main thing was that he had access to Scott Taylor. And I reckoned if he could drop a hint or two in the direction of that hunky lovely then I was away.

I decided the next school football match was a good place to start. Dave nearly fell out of his pram. I hated football, he squawked — and as luck would have it, just as Scott Taylor came round the corner, too. No, I didn't, I said, the moment I knew that Scott was within earshot. I reckoned it was a real man's game. But I couldn't be sure that Scott had heard me.

I thought I saw him glance over, so it seemed like the time to drive home a good impression. I couldn't understand what Dave found so funny about me asking how many tries the school had got in their last game, but then he always did have a weird sense of humour. Then I said that I was looking forward to the game on Saturday and gave Scott Taylor one of my winning smiles as I swanned off past him along the corridor. Not that he noticed unfortunately, 'cos Cheryl Thomas waltzed in from the opposite direction at that moment and heads always turned when she was about. Still, I didn't care. I reckoned I'd already made a good impression on Scott with my knowledge of the game. The rest would be easy, wouldn't it?

WHY are football matches always played in sub-zero temperatures? It was terrible thinking that I could have been tucked up nice and warm in bed instead of standing on that touchline in the local park yelling out, "Come on St Joseph's!" at the top of my voice and no one taking any notice of me anyway. Except Dave who kept me company near the goalmouth.

"Come on, Scott!" I yelled. "It's an open goal!" He threw me an odd sort of glance and gave the ball a very gentle tap, straight into the arms of the guy in the green vest.

"He didn't try very hard there," I said to Dave, who was giving me this strange look.

"That's 'cos it's our goalie," he said. "We usually try to get the ball past the other team's."

"Oh," I croaked and felt myself going bright red. This wasn't going to help my chances with Scott much. I began thinking of all that chocolate I'd given up. Not that I'd noticed much difference in the scales. And I was feeling dead miserable, too. It was only the thought of Scott sweeping me into his arms at full-time that kept me from caving in there and then and snatching the last bit of Dave's Mars bar.

That was when I spotted Cheryl Thomas, the girl with everything a boy could want and all in the right places, too. What was she doing here? I felt this sick thud in my stomach and

the shock must have sent me reeling. Then Dave was looking into my eyes and asking if I was all right and I realised that some clown had walloped the ball straight at me.

"Which stupid idiot did that?" I shouted, then went into a dead swoon as Scott came rushing over. He'd seen me fall and was hurrying to comfort me.

"Can we have the ball back?" he asked.

I opened one eye. He was already walking away, the ball tucked securely under his arm. I couldn't believe it. Then he turned and called back.

"Don't stand so close to the touchline," he said. "I might hit the ball harder next time."

So he'd done it! The rat! I felt Dave slip a comforting arm around my shoulder.

"I feel so stupid," I murmured. "And everyone was looking at me, too."

" 'Course they weren't," said Dave sweetly, but I could tell he was just trying to be nice.

I was just beginning to feel really sorry for myself when there was a shout from the pitch.

Scott was rolling on the ground, clutching his leg, surrounded by team-mates and trainers. Suddenly my troubles didn't seem so bad. Scott was hurt. Now, he would need me by his side. So why was Cheryl rushing forward and not me? It didn't take too many 'O' levels to suss that one out!

By now they were carrying Scott off the field. He was holding his leg and moaning, while Cheryl was fussing all over him. Dave was smiling, and suddenly I didn't feel so miserable anymore.

"What's so funny?" I asked. "Scott could be hurt."

Dave shook his head.

"No, he's not. He's playing up. Acting the fallen hero. He's after Cheryl."

"He is?" I couldn't believe my ears.

"Yeah. He's been trying to go out with her for months. He's just found out she wants to be a nurse when she leaves school, so he thought if he pulled something like this, he'd finally get her attention."

"So how come she's here, anyway?" I asked dimly.

"Because she fancies him, too, only with his reputation she doesn't want to be seen chasing him, does she?"

"No . . . I . . . em, suppose not," I croaked.

"Well, you wouldn't do it, would you?"

"Oh, never!" I shrieked. "I mean . . . em . . . no," I said a bit more quietly.

It was a neat plan. I could appreciate it. There was just one flaw in Scott's scheme. He was only supposed to pretend to be hurt. But it turned out he'd fallen awkwardly and torn the ligaments of his left leg. Which was bad news for Scott but great news for Dave. He was in the team at last.

If Dave was happy then, he was even happier when he came off forty minutes later, having scored both tries . . . em . . . I mean goals in the school's 2-1 win. At this rate it looked like he might be in the team for some time to come.

I WENT home and decided to feel dead miserable for the rest of the year. If I'd had any money I'd have bought some chocolates and drowned my sorrow in some soft centres.

But I needn't have worried. Half an hour later the bell rang and there was Dave standing on the doorstep, looking very pleased with himself and clutching a box of my favourite chocs. I virtually fell at his feet!

"You're not really on a diet, are you?" he asked a few minutes later as I tucked into a mouth-watering Turkish delight.

" 'Course not," I grunted, through a mouthful of chocolate. "Whatever gave you that idea?"

"That's good," he replied, "because I like you just the way you are . . ."

I looked into his eyes and there was something there I'd never seen before. Or maybe it had always been there and I just hadn't bothered to take notice. I was too busy wasting my time with the likes of Scott Taylor.

"Resolutions! Pah!" I sniffed. "Who needs 'em?"

"Oh, I don't know," said Dave, "I made a couple."

"Me, too," I said, biting into another chocolate, "and not one of them worked out. I've broken them both already. How did yours go, then?"

"Fine," he said. "One was to get into the football team, and I've done that now, thanks to Cheryl Thomas."

"I know. Well done," I said. "And the other?"

"Oh, that," he murmured, slipping his arm around my shoulder and snuggling a bit closer. "I'm working on that one . . ."

I'd loused up my resolutions, but somehow it didn't seem to matter anymore. I reckoned that Dave's were probably going to be enough for both of us . . .

That was a year ago.

And I was right . . .

WHAT'S YOUR BAG?

BAGGED!

So what do Mr or Ms Joe Bloggs in the street use to carry their gear? Let's find out . . .!

Joan "Ooer-you're-not-photographing-me!" Gingham

"This is my daytime bag. Nice, innit? It's perfect for carrying my bare essentials, i.e. my make-up and cheque book! I've got a smaller version for night-time. I couldn't do without my bag, it's permanently glued to my shoulder."

Nicky Mathieson and Brian Quinn

Brian: "Handbag? No Way! Duffle bag? Probably — I'd carry Nicky's bag anytime."

(Aaaaawww!)

Nicky: "I'm a duffle bag or rucksack girl, they're really comfy to use. Inside I've got some money (lucky girl!), a brolly and my make-up. Pretty boring, I know."

Gail and Sharon Rattray, Ann Taylor

"We all like the same type of bags — just a shoulder bag, not too big, with maybe just one pocket on the inside."

—Looks like there's a bit of truth in the 'family thinking alike' school of thought, eh, Gail?

"Yes, it's a bit embarrassing but we both ended up getting exactly the same type of bag. We try not to stand together!"

Sharon Glenn

"My bag's a black leather one — I hate teensy tottie ones but this is just big enough for a can of hairspray and some make-up: I'd never be without them!"

—How would you feel about your boyfriend carrying a handbag?

"He'd be chucked! Guys shouldn't have bags, it looks *really* stupid!"

Tracey Stewart

"I love rucksacks and duffle bags, you can take them anywhere. I use this one for school, though today it's got my shopping in it. The best thing is that I can keep my hands free and the clutter's contained in one area: you never know what you'll find at the bottom of this bag — there's lots of remnants of days gone by down in the depths of it!"

George Robb, postie

—Like the bag, Mr Postman!

"Well, it's all part of the job really but I'm quite attached to it. Today it's got a few parcels in it, but usually it's dead heavy."

(Looks heavy enough to us — oooer!)

Lynn Buntin and Ewen "Never-playing -rugby-again" Robertson

Lynn: "I *hate* bags, I possess not one! My trusty coat is equipped with many a pocket so I jingle all along the road. In any case, I've got enough on my hands right now trying to stop Ewen from keeling over!"

Ewen: "Would I carry a handbag? We-eeeel, not an ickle-pritty flowery one but I might cope with a rucksack. I just stuff things in my pocket. Thank goodness I don't use make-up!"

14

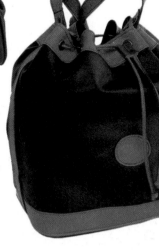

Whether you're a rucksack gal or a clutchbag chick, there's a very sensible reason for it — or is there? We decided to find out...

Karen Duncan

—Why no handbag, Karen?

"Well, actually I normally carry one but I was in such a rush today that I just threw everything into my pockets and ran out. My normal one is very small, with a long, long strap — just big enough to put my purse in."

A conversation overheard in a shop . . .

"Hey, Josie, what a fabbo bag!"

"Quite groovesome, isn't it? Strange really, this geezer just came along one day and dumped it on my shoulder. I'm not complaining, though, it's perfect to carry the essentials of life, like my thumbscrew, my Swiss bank account book and my teddy bear."

"Hmm, do you think if I stick about for long enough, they might give me one, too?"

"Probably — you could give it a try."

"OK, see you around sometime — oooer! What's this guy doing pulling off my trousers?!"

THE HARD CASE

Wow! If you're a briefcase girl you knock the socks off everyone you meet, you're super-duper-efficient! You know what you want and where you're going, and nothing or nobody is gonna stand in your way. We are talking ambition here! An aspiring Yuppy, you'll have at least one purse, a Filofax, some writing paper and train timetables. Sounds boring? Not one bit of it, you've got lots of friends and love to socialise — after you're sure you've done all the other things you've got to do. If you relaxed a bit more, though, maybe you wouldn't give such an ice-cool image?

THE CLUTCH BAG CHICK

If you see a beanpole-legged, stiletto-heeled, two-piece suited female with luscious locks of peroxide or dark brown hair coming towards you, let your eyes drop to her hands and there, sure as fate, will be a clutch bag. She's got a steady, dependable job and she likes nothing better after hours than going to discos with her boyfriend or seeing her one or two close girlfriends. Anyone who carries a bag like this is extra-specially confident of her looks: not for her the ten tins of hairspray and half-a-chemist's-shop-full of make-up! Inside she'll probably have a comb, her purse and a lipstick — what an efficient girl! Her only failing is, when she goes to the disco, sometimes — just sometimes — she's caught dancing round her bag: what a let down!

THE BIG BAG

And here we have chaos and disorder at its loveable best! Paper hankies (used and unused — yeuchh!), pens — at least six — cartoons cut out of newspapers, old letters, loose change, loose (and very dirty) items of make-up, scribbled-down lists and phone numbers — you name it, here's where you'll find it. The girl who carries around a bag like this has no time for finicking around with clips or drawstrings, she just chucks everything in willy-nilly so she can get on with other things. She's always surrounded by loads of friends and likes nothing better than spending hours in cafés having a giggle with them. In short, the gal who loves a big bag is just a bundle of fun!

 15

THE RUCKSACK RAVER

The rucksack for everyday use was first fashionable on the continent: and that says it all. This gal's got style with a capital S, and doesn't she know it! If you delve further into her wardrobe you'll probably find more classics like ripped denims and the obligatory Doc Martens. She never goes anywhere without her Walkman, and probably there'll also be a book or two inside her bag. If there's any make-up at all, it'll probably be some face powder. She's into hip-hop and Terence Trent D'Arby, and when she goes out it's usually for lunch or dinner — she's a very healthy eater, so no choccie bars for her, nosirree! If she's got a fault at all, it's probably that she *knows* she's not got any faults. Sickening isn't it?

BLUE JEANS
►HUNK No.1◄
Rick Astley

OLD FAVOURITES

Ever wondered what the BJ gang are really like? Are they ageing hippies or trendee young things? Here's where you find out the truth 'cos they've opened their doors and revealed their most personal possessions!

FIONA

"I definitely couldn't live without this little lot! There's my camera to snap sexy guys with. Irn Bru (I drink at least three cans of it per day!), the socks are v.v. high up on my fave list and are never off my feet. (Eugh, what a smelly pig! — The Ed.)

"I love Lloyd Cole and the Commotions so 'Rattlesnakes' is a must.

"Now for the pretentious bit — Bourjois make-up and Chanel No. 5! Well, why not? I've got pots of money! (Ooer! — BJ gang.)

"The case is from Paris and makes me feel dead grown up and businesslike!"

JACQUIE

"The peanut butter's there because it's the scrummiest stuff ever — mmmm! Lou Reed and Billy Bragg are my heroes, so their albums are a must, and I like the Flesh For Lulu 12 inch because it's a cheery little ditty, good for stompin' about to.

"The yellow shirt belonged to an ex-lover of mine (!), the tatty but loveable jacket was a third-hand gift from another, and if anyone in this office says anything, I'll thump them... The jewellery box was a present from a friend who went to India for a holiday, and it holds all my favourite gems. The scarves are there because I'm a hippy head as anyone'll tell you.

"The water pistol's actually a laser-powered ray-gun that ole Zody Mindwarpson left at my flat after one of his visits... I'll shut up now, OK?"

17

VAL

"Happiness is being on holiday. Add to that the sounds of Bryan Ferry, Leonard Cohen or even Beethoven (!) on a personal stereo, a good book to read and a HUGE sarnie to munch and I'm ecstatic! My fave holiday destinations are many and varied. Sun, sand and sea aren't even obligatory (i.e. I sometimes holiday in good ole G.B.!).

"Food faves are far too numerous to be explicit, hence the variety of cookery books. I lurve eating so much that I'm actually prepared to spend many an hour slaving over a hot stove to titillate my taste buds.

"The bar of Toblerone's here 'cos not only is it yummy to eat, it also melts down to make a fantastic choccy sauce to pour over ice-cream. Mmmm!

"I'm quite a plant person, too, and this specimen is a favourite.

"The books I've selected here are 'The Sandcastle' by Iris Murdoch and Charlotte Bronte's classic lurve story 'Jane Eyre'.

"But my most favourite thing in the whole wide world is Bracken, my golden retriever doggie — isn't she just the cutest thing?!"

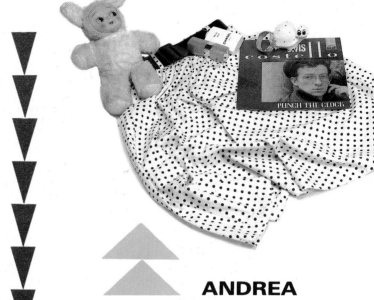

ANDREA

"Well, you can see why this skirt is a favourite — can't you? I bought it in a sale last summer for a fiver and I've never stopped wearing it since.

"Then there's my Chanel 19 talc and perfume which I never go anywhere without; the cute tortoise bankie which was a present from a best friend; the bracelet, a great reminder of my birthday in Morocco when I visited the Casbah, and the furry-thing, a pressie for my first birthday (aaah . . .).

"The Elvis Costello album I like because it holds many a happy memory for me — but that's another story . . ."

18

GAYLE

"Here they are — my favourite things in the whole wide world and Africa!

"I bought these trusty ol' jeans 8 years ago when I was but a babe in arms, and although they're getting a bit draughty round the knee and bottom areas, I won't buy a new pair. (Basically, because I'm too mean!) Aye, me and those jeans have seen some good times together ... (Oh, no give us a break, purlease!! — The entire BJ gang.)

"The book is a specially illustrated edition by my favourite author, Laurie Lee. It's groovy — and far better for you than saucy, steamy Jackie Collins novelettes — so there!

"The rather attractive green jersey and black shorts are for my favourite hobby — no, not boogieing on down at the disco, cycling, you fools!

"These veggie burgers are truly sloosome, especially if you're an earth momma like me.

"The albums are by Sam Cooke (I liked him *long* before the recent revival 'cos I'm extremely hip, OK?) (or extremely old, haw, haw — ver gang.) and Ted Hawkins — both are made for late night smoochin' with a glass of Tizer by your side.

"The key is for my house — because I love it and it's my favourite possession and I don't care if you think I'm a yuppie."

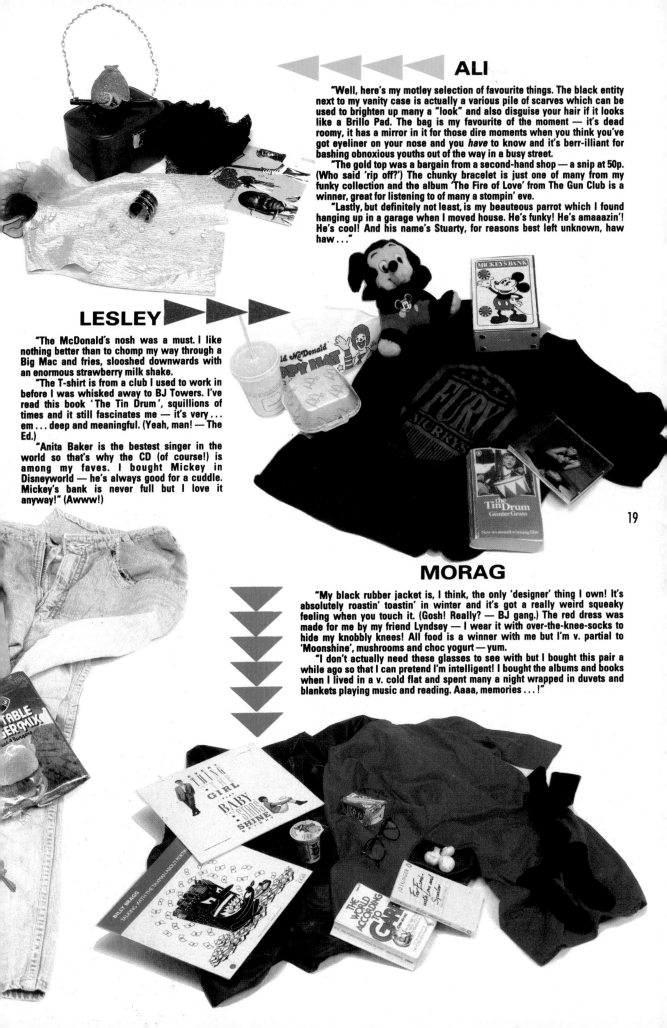

ALI

"Well, here's my motley selection of favourite things. The black entity next to my vanity case is actually a various pile of scarves which can be used to brighten up many a "look" and also disguise your hair if it looks like a Brillo Pad. The bag is my favourite of the moment — it's dead roomy, it has a mirror in it for those dire moments when you think you've got eyeliner on your nose and you *have* to know and it's berr-illiant for bashing obnoxious youths out of the way in a busy street.

"The gold top was a bargain from a second-hand shop — a snip at 50p. (Who said 'rip off?') The chunky bracelet is just one of many from my funky collection and the album 'The Fire of Love' from The Gun Club is a winner, great for listening to of many a stompin' eve.

"Lastly, but definitely not least, is my beauteous parrot which I found hanging up in a garage when I moved house. He's funky! He's amaaazin'! He's cool! And his name's Stuarty, for reasons best left unknown, haw haw . . ."

LESLEY

"The McDonald's nosh was a must. I like nothing better than to chomp my way through a Big Mac and fries, slooshed downwards with an enormous strawberry milk shake.

"The T-shirt is from a club I used to work in before I was whisked away to BJ Towers. I've read this book 'The Tin Drum', squillions of times and it still fascinates me — it's very . . . em . . . deep and meaningful. (Yeah, man! — The Ed.)

"Anita Baker is the bestest singer in the world so that's why the CD (of course!) is among my faves. I bought Mickey in Disneyworld — he's always good for a cuddle. Mickey's bank is never full but I love it anyway!" (Awww!)

19

MORAG

"My black rubber jacket is, I think, the only 'designer' thing I own! It's absolutely roastin' toastin' in winter and it's got a really weird squeaky feeling when you touch it. (Gosh! Really? — BJ gang.) The red dress was made for me by my friend Lyndsey — I wear it with over-the-knee-socks to hide my knobbly knees! All food is a winner with me but I'm v. partial to 'Moonshine', mushrooms and choc yogurt — yum.

"I don't actually need these glasses to see with but I bought this pair a while ago so that I can pretend I'm intelligent! I bought the albums and books when I lived in a v. cold flat and spent many a night wrapped in duvets and blankets playing music and reading. Aaaa, memories . . . !"

BROS: THE FACTS

DID YOU KNOW THAT CRAIG SAYS 'BASICALLY' ALL THE TIME, LUKE'S SCARED OF GETTING HIS HANDS CUT OFF AND MATT'S NOT V. CONFIDENT OF CHATTING UP THE GIRLIES? YOU DIDN'T? WELL, READ ON AND FIND OUT MANY ANOTHER STONKING SNIPPET . . .

- Matt and Luke Goss were born in Lewisham, London on September 29, 1968.

- Luke is the elder by ten minutes!

- Craig Logan was born in Kirkcaldy, Fife on March 22, 1969.

- Matt sometimes thinks he's really ugly . . . what?!! "I sometimes say to Craig, 'Oh no, I look like a real piggy today,'" says the lad, who's really not-very-ugly at all.

- Matt cried his eyes out when he saw 'The Color Purple' — what a cutie!

- Bros earned the dubious honour of being the first band to have a single put in Radio One's 'sin-bin'. The 'sin-bin', in case you're not familiar with it, is how the BBC referred to their clamp-down on the playing of records that aren't play-listed. Before "When Will I Be Famous" was on the play list, mega-trendy Simon Bates played it and got a slapped wrist for it!

- Bros don't want to be thought of as pretty boys — they might have many a girlie after their bods, but they want to be thought of first and foremost as talented musicians and songwriters.

- The twins' grandad sings in old people's homes and is 'really wicked'.

- They all have lots of girlies following them around and absolutely lurve being recognised!

- They say the reaction they get from their fans is 'like a dream' and they wish they had time to talk to them all! Cute boys, eh?

- Craig once sent a love poem to someone, but we couldn't worm any more out of him!

- Matt says that if he goes out with a girl he believes in total fidelity. "I hate anyone who double-crosses another person," he says. "It's OK to *look* at other girls — but don't ever touch! If I went out with a girl and she even kissed another boy, that would be it." Ooh, scarey!

- Craig's a big believer in love at first sight!

- When the band first got together they played in a lot of working men's clubs. "We had quite an embarrassing time of it," says Matt. "Whenever we finished a number it would take about a minute for it to sink in and then they'd clap for about four seconds." Changed days, indeed.

- Luke has a fear of his hands being chopped off, Craig's fairly scared of beasties and crawlies and Matthew's not too happy with the thought of a nuclear war.

- Luke's a big Lenny Henry fan.

- Bros' first single "I Owe You Nothing", is now a collector's item. Only a limited number of copies were pressed and it was distributed throughout clubs and it soon became a big cult fave.

- The first gig Craig went to see was AC/DC when he was 11, which he says, is now truly embarrassing.

- Bros have been together since they were 14!

- They all argue over really silly things. "We might argue about something like Craig having more food than me. He'll come round to dinner and I have to say 'Mum, you've given more pie to Craig than me and I'm your son'," says Luke.

- They can all stuff their faces to their hearts' content without putting on an ounce of weight . . . just like the BJ gang, har de har har!

- Luke loves eating out. "Mexican, British, Indian, Italian — you name it, I'll eat it," he says.

- Matt loves spending Sunday mornings in bed.

- Craig says 'basically' all the time.

- Matt's the least confident when it comes to chatting up the girlies! He reckons one of the most important qualities in a prospective girlfriend isn't good looks, but someone with a funky sense of humour.

- Matt and Luke used to love Rod Stewart's hair! They get their own barnets cut every four weeks.

- 'Airplane' is one of Matt's favourite films and they all love Eddie Murphy.

- They're a v. good-looking and talented combo and we think they'll be around for many years. Yo!

FAKE IT OR LEAVE IT!

Black "Snakeskin" bag from Top Shop.

Leopard print scarf and twisted pearl necklace from Top Shop.

Fancy a quick change of image but don't want to make it permanent? Well, check out these fabby fakes for inspiration!

22

Instant tan, skin tint and stocking cream by No 7. Available from Boots.

"Tortoiseshell" combs and bangle from a selection at Top Shop.

Silk rosebuds from many a good florist or department store.

Teapot clock from a range at British Home Stores.

Cutesy, cutesy tiger slippers from Top Shop.

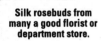

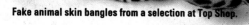

Fake animal skin bangles from a selection at Top Shop.

Blue and red fake fur hats from a selection at British Home Stores.

Selection of hair dyes from Boots.

Just the thing to make an impression — false nails. From Boots.

"Snakeskin" belts from Top Shop.

Funky black spikey wig, guaranteed to give your mum heart failure! By Carmen, available from Arnotts.

23

WHY bother wasting time and money cultivating natural beauty when it takes less time and costs less to fake it?! Many of the fakes around nowadays can look real if you want them to, like false nails. You can buy actual false nails or nail tips, kits to paint on beautiful long nails or go to a beauty salon and sit about like Lady Muck and have someone else do it for you!

False hair pieces and ponytails can look très chic and realistic if you choose a colour close to your own hair, or if you want to look dramatic and different go for wacky, multicoloured wigs or hair extensions!

Imitation jewellery is another big hit in the world of fakes. In fact, many a mega rich person in possession of a collection of glittering jewels has an identical collection of fakes for everyday wear and keeps the real ones in the safe! But for the normal average lass diamanté and fake pearls can be just as effective as the real thing!

If you don't have pots of money to spend on a mink coat, fear not, 'cos a purple false fur with big black spots on it is trendier and leaves you with a clear conscience, too!

Whether you want to go for a completely different look or want to make life a bit more interesting, or even just for a bit of a laugh, there's a fake out there for you!!

Just the thing for a long trek round the golf course— chocolate golf balls by Fisher and Donaldson.

Ever fancied hanging a few springs from your head? Blonde (and very curly!) false ponytail by Carmen. Available from Arnotts.

Leopard print hair bow and pearl necklace and bracelets all from Top Shop.

Skirt, socks and bow from Chelsea Girl.

1

2

Be bold, be blasé, be bright, but most of all be totally RAD. Freak them out — stripe out!

STRIPE-TEASE!

1. Skirt, black/white striped top, braces, socks and rucksack from Top Shop. Black shoes from Schuh.

2. Shorts, cropped navy stripey jumper and red jumper from Top Shop. Shoes and socks from Chelsea Girl. Rucksack as before.

Stripey shirts from Top Shop.

Top & vest from Chelsea Girl.
Shoes from Top Shop.

Stripey T-shirts from Top Shop.

Stripey rucksack from
Chelsea Girl.

3

4

3. All from Chelsea Girl.
4. Red skirt from Top Shop.
Stripey T-shirt from Chelsea Girl.
Shoes from Schuh. Tights from The
Sock Shop. Jacket, model's own.

SCHOOL STREET INTERVIEWS

Are school days really the best days of our lives? Or do you walk around in a 'school daze'?! (Har-de-har har!) Yet again our intrepid reporters took to the streets . . .

ANGIE HALFORD

Are you still at school?
Yes, I'm still there, studying hard of course! (Said with a suspicious smirk, ahem!)
Do you like it?
Yeah, believe it or not, I do! Mind you, I want to be a mechanic when I leave, and because it's such a tough business for a girl to break into, it means I have to swot really hard so I get good results. That's the bad side of school, I suppose!

TINA HALFORD

Are you still at school?
No, I've just left to do dentistry.
Did you like it when you were there?
Yes — dunno about the work side of things, but it was great being in a crowd of friends all day and having loads of laughs.

KAMINI PAUL

Are you still at school?
No, I'm at university, doing bio-chemistry. (Cripes!)
Did you enjoy school?
It was OK, I suppose. I was quite glad to leave though, and I'm enjoying university a lot more — you're treated like a proper adult, which is great.

the best days of your life?

Are you a girlie swot, or one of the kids the teacher doesn't like to mention? Or maybe you're not even at school anymore? We decided to swot up on this whole school business . . .

KERRY SHANNON

Are you still at school?
No, I left a short while ago, and I'm an apprentice hairdresser now.
Did you like school when you were there?
Um . . . it was all right, but I was pretty glad when I walked out of the gates for the last time! Me and some of the teachers didn't see eye-to-eye on a few things, shall we say . . . (Less said about that the better, methinks!)

SUSAN LAING

Are you still at school?
Yes, I'm still there, but I'm leaving to join the police force soon.
Do you enjoy it?
Most of the time, it's fine. There's the odd hassle of course, and no one likes homework, but all in all, it's OK.

THOMAS RAMSAY

Are you still at school?
No, I'm an apprentice baker now.
Did you like school?
Well, it was OK I suppose, but I didn't much like the power the teachers had over everyone — I think sometimes it was too much.

ALISON JOYCE

Are you still a school-girlie, then?
Nope, I've got a job in a department store.
Did you like school?
No, I hated it! I didn't get on with any of my teachers, you see, and I hated being treated like a little kid all the time.

GRANT DUFF

Are you still at school?
(Takes offence.) Definitely not! I'm a trainee chef, actually. (Sorry we spoke!)
Did you like it when you were there?
I don't think anyone likes school when they're there — I hated it, but I still sometimes wish I was back there, and I bet most people feel the same, if they'd only admit it.

GRANT WILKIE

Are you still at school, Grant?
No, I'm training to be a primary school teacher.
Did you like school?
Nah, I hated it. I just didn't get on with any of the people there — it was an awful place, I was really glad to leave, and I never want to go back there. (Oh, c'mon, Grant, say what you mean . . . ! By the way, we think you're a cute boy . . .)

27

Bono didn't like his Spanish teacher — he lobbed doggie pooh over a hedge on to her. (Blee!!) Shortly afterwards, he left school. Quelle surprise, eh?

Clark Datchler from Johnny Hates Jazz went to public school: "I don't think public school suited me. The attitude to pop music was very stern, it was very much frowned upon. So after 'O' levels I left . . . and I failed my music 'O' level!"

Carol Decker was 19 (cripes!) when she left school because she had to re-take all her exams. There's hope for us all yet, chicks . . .

Jason 'Robin of Sherwood' Connery went to Gordonstoun Public School (a v. posh indeed school, also attended by HRH Prince Charles). Ooooer! He liked sports, but maths and stuff weren't exactly his fave-o subjects. Still, he left aged 17, with six 'O'-levels, so things can't have been too bad!

Mark Shaw's (Then Jerico) dad moved around a lot when Mark was young, so he went to many a different school. "Because of that, I didn't really spend an awful lot of time developing friendships. As I got a bit older I became very brash as a cover-up, but underneath it all I was quite shy."

Michael J. Fox always knew he was 'born to act', so he left high school before he finished all his final exams. "The funny thing was, I failed drama, even though I was doing a TV series AND a stage show at the same time!"

George Michael v. probably wouldn't be where he is today (who said, "I wish"?!) if he hadn't met one Andrew Ridgeley at Bushey Meads Comprehensive. Andrew was a 'birrova lad', and it was him who talked Georgie into forming a band.

Dolph 'I dated Grace Jones and lived to tell the tale' Lundgren was a skinny runt at school — hard to credit it, hmmm? "I was the clown that would do yucky things, like take a dead rat and throw it on some girl's desk." Worra lark, eh? Must've been quite a brainy lad, though, 'cos he speaks fluent English and German, as well as his native Swedish.

GIRLIE SWOTS

Chris Lowe (Pet Shop Boys)
Carol Decker
Corinne (Swing Out Sister)
Dolph Lundgren
Jonathan King (had to have something going for him, haw, haw!)
Most of Then Jerico
Freddie Mercury and the rest of Queen

TUFF TYKES

Bobbity Geldof
Tom Cruise
Nick Berry
The Proclaimers
Sam Fox
Bruce Willis
Ben from Curiosity

SCENTIMENTAL!

Deciding on a perfume isn't easy, so let us help you make up your mind with our guide to smelling good — it makes perfect scents!

Sporty

Perfume is an invisible form of make-up you just shouldn't be without.

The right fragrance can give you an air of mystery, class or romance — even if you're not dressed up to the nines!

For centuries, both women and men have considered nice scents to be as important as their clothes, make-up or hairstyles — and things haven't changed!

Nowadays, people are willing to pay anything from about £2.50 to over £1,000 for their "special" perfume!

But even if you're willing to pay the earth for a fragrance that everyone's raving about, it may not necessarily smell very good on you.

That's why you should test a perfume thoroughly before buying — especially if you're intending to spend a considerable amount of money on it!

Don't be put off by the huge choice of testers and all the fancy packaging — take your time, and remember, it's not the packaging you're going to wear.

After trying a tester perfume on at the counter, wait half an hour before deciding whether you're going to buy it. It takes time for the perfume to warm up and react with the acids present in your skin.

Remember that a perfume, no matter how it smells in the bottle, can smell very different on each person who wears it.

If you don't want to stick to wearing the same perfume day and night, you can choose from various types of scent to suit your different moods.

Fruity fragrances are ideal for sporty days and for

The Lemon Verbena fragrance from The Body Shop's range of perfume oil is worn by the sporty, nature-loving girl. She's full of energy and vitality and loves a natural, fresh, fruity scent. Lemon Verbena is ideal for her as it's subtly sweet with an overtone of tangy lemon. As it's an oil, she can rely on this scent to last throughout her busy day.

The citrus zing of the fragrance keeps her fresh during those vigorous games of squash or the long jogs around the park. The sweet tones of Lemon Verbena also reflect her lively character at parties and on days out with her friends.

casual, everyday occasions when you want to stay fresh but subtly feminine.

Check out the Body Shop's range of scents — they include a number of fruity fragrances which smell good enough to eat!

For those lazy Sunday afternoons, hopeless romantics should go for a soft, flowery fragrance. They're just the thing to wear when you and your beloved are gazing into each other's eyes!

You'll find there are a wide range of test perfumes available from most of the larger chemists and department stores. Look out for the fragrances by Cacharel or Max Factor.

Girls who love the great outdoors should go for bright and breezy scents — a must for those long walks along the beach with the love of your life!

Test out some of the perfumes by Yves St Laurent or Revlon.

When you want to make dramatic impressions on those special nights out, give yourself a touch of mystery with a sultry, sexy fragrance.

If you've plenty of money, try Christian Dior, or alternatively one or two of the top range Max Factor scents.

Whichever perfume you decide upon, don't use too much of it — no matter how much you love it! A subtle aroma is much more attractive than choking great clouds of perfume which simply make people gag!

Clashing fragrances are just as bad, so make sure you wash away any traces of a daytime perfume before using a different scent in the evening.

Try and co-ordinate your bath goodies and lotion with your perfume by saving up for the full range of products in your favourite scent.

Avoid buying strong-smelling hairsprays and deodorants which may also spoil the full effect of your perfume.

CONTINUED ON P30

The incurable romantic will always fall for a perfume like Le Jardin de Max Factor. The delicate floral scent is perfect for those dreamy days spent with her ideal boy.

The Le Jardin girl loves to look as romantic as possible, with soft, natural make-up and shiny, billowing hair.

The fresh, spring fragrance is created using a blend of Bergamot, Tagete and Peach with warm notes of Jasmin, Rose and Magnolia.

The lingering base which gives the scent its delicate femininity consists of a mixture of Amber, Cedar and Myrrh with just a hint of Musk.

29

Romantic

CONTINUED FROM P29

SCENT SAVERS

Get your money's worth from your perfume by taking a few of the following tips:

* Store your perfume in a cool, dark place. Strong sunlight can make a perfume evaporate more quickly — and it'll go off.

* Try and use your perfume as often as possible after the seal is broken — saving it for those extra special occasions isn't being thrifty, as it'll evaporate anyway.

* Don't throw away your empties! Even if you've finished the perfume the fragrance will still linger, so remove the lids and keep the bottles in your underwear drawer!

* Spraying a little scent in the right places can have as good an effect as scooshing it about your person. Use it on your pulse points (i.e. your neck, behind the ears, wrists, backs of your knees, and your ankles). If you're wearing a thin scarf or a high collar, a dab or two of perfume on your neck will go a long way.

* Don't waste perfume during the warm weather by wearing it before sunbathing. Not only could you end up smelling rather odd, but the UVA rays in sunlight can react with the perfume to make you break out in a rash. And you're not exactly going to appear sultry or mysterious when you're covered in angry red blotches, are you? Don't wear perfume under a sunbed either, as the effect will be the same.

Girls who love the great outdoors will never be without Blasé by Max Factor.

The bright, youthful fragrance is ideal for wearing on those carefree days with friends or the special evenings spent with that extra-special boy.

The Blasé girl loves the refreshing scent which helps her keep her cool on those long walks with the love of her life!

The sweet base note is a blend of sandalwood and honey and is followed up with a cool middle note of carnation and jasmin with a top note of raspberry and bergamot.

The perfect blend of fragrances gives perfect style to the lively, but casual, Blasé girl.

Perfume was probably first used by the ancient Egyptians who burned aromatic woods for their fragrant smoke.

The word "perfume" originates from the Latin word "per" which means "through" and "fumus" which means "smoke".

Egyptian men were buried with jars of perfume oil so that they smelled nice in the after-life!

Perfume was then a sign of wealth, and was also used in religious ceremonies.

Although perfume is now very widely used, it can still be a sign of wealth and success. Very rich ladies are often willing to spend large amounts of money to have a perfume made especially for them!

Perfume oil can be very expensive to make — especially if the ingredients are difficult to obtain. To make just one jar of jasmin oil, over two million petals are needed!

A perfumer, who designs a fragrance sometimes from hundreds of ingredients, has to have a very delicate sense of smell. He or she is considered to be as much an artist as a scientist, as the finished perfume has to be as individual and exciting as any famous painting.

31

Woman of Mystery

The girl who loves to leave a dramatic impression on those special dates, wears Epris. She likes to be mysterious but sultry and attractive at the same time.

The spicy, eastern ingredients of the scent helps the Epris girl become unforgettable.

She's ambitious and outgoing and loves being a girl!

Even if she's just wearing a pair of old jeans, she's never without Epris.

The fragrance is long-lasting and sophisticated with a semi-Oriental floral blend of ylang ylang, ouillet, muguet, rose and mimosa. Carnation, basil, clove and coriander form the spicy sensuous notes, together with touches of aromatic woods, mosses and amber.

THE Blue Jeans AWARDS

FANFARE! DRUM ROLL! YUSS, IT'S THAT TIME AGAIN — TIME TO SEE WHO'S SHOT TO THE TOP AND WHO'S MADE A PROPER WALLY OF THEMSELVES . . .

BEST-DRESSED BOY-ABOUT-TOWN:

Jonathan Woss is the obvious choice here. Those suits! Those sharp ties! A well-put-together young gentleman if ever there was one, yesirree!

SILLIEST LADS:

Marti and the other Wetties get this award — worra loada clowns, eh? There's nary a time when they're not up to their jolly japes and frolicks. A well-deserved award, indeed!

DIRTIEST ROCKER ABOUT TOWN:

Zodiac Mindwarp. Yup, the Zode man's gotta walk away with this one. Don't get us wrong now — we love olde Zode from the top of his matted head to the soles of his grubby feet, but the man is FILTHY!!

SPOTTIEST PERSON:

Ben from Curiosity. Sorry dearie, but you **are** Zit City . . .

BEST (?) HAIRCUT:

Haw haw! A touch of the ole BJ sarkiness a-creeping in, methinks . . . we nominate Brucie Willis for this one. And the prize? A year's supply of Baby Bio, to help his poor locks grow a bit.

PERSON(S) WE'D MOST LIKE TO GO KISSY-KISSY WITH:

Terence Trent D'Arbington has to come top of the heap here, but there's many a runner up, too . . . C Thomas Howell (does the 'C' stand for cute, we wonder??), and sleazoid ole Mickey Rourke . . . any man who owns a red Ferrari/lots of dosh/a sweet shop . . . and a thousand more . . .

BESTEST LEGS IN POP:

Whitters Houston sweeps the board in this one, and makes us all feel sick sick sick with jealousy. Especially when said pins are teamed with the rest of Whitney's assets . . . Huh!

MOST SLOO-SOME SWEETIE:

Milky Bar Buttons — need we say more?

PERSON(S) WE'D LEAST LIKE TO GO KISSY-KISSY WITH:

Shane MacGowan — cute, but oh, those teeth! Kiefer Sutherland (scary) and Mick Hucknall (downright ugly) are the proud (?) runners up.

GLOOMIEST POPSTER:

Difficult, very difficult . . . a toss-up between Clark "Stone-Face" Datchler and Colin "Wet-Weekend" Vearncomb. Think ole Clark steals it, though — at least Colin sings about a "Wonderful Life" . . .

HAIRIEST PERSON:

A tough one, this . . . after some minutes' thought . . . well, it's gotta be David Coverdale from Whitesnake, hasn't it? Those flowing locks would put any girlie to shame, they surely would.

SPECKIEST PEOPLE IN POP:

The Proclaimers! Nae contest, as the Auchtermuchty laddies themselves would say.

FOXIEST CHICK:

Everyone in the office had a different suggestion here, but we finally settled for Madonna, because she's had many a different image but she still always manages to get the guys a-flocking after her . . . life's not fair!

33

BESTEST MAGAZINE:

Well, it's obvious, innit? Who keeps you entertained, informed and gives you all the sauciest gossip around? Blue Jeans of course! Yippee!

MOST DRASTIC CHANGE OF IMAGE:

Those baby-faced boppers, Bros, weren't always the spike-o smoothies they are today . . . check those flowing, curlsome locks . . . Blee!!

THE HOUND of the BASKA VILLAS

Shirley Holmes had just been accepted on a YTS scheme — as a private detective!

NICE TO MEET YOU, SHIRLEY.

WELCOME TO THE TEAM, SHIRLEY. THIS IS JEFF WATSON. HE'LL BE SHOWING YOU THE ROPES.

YOU TOO, JEFF.

WOW! JEFF'S REALLY CUTE. I THINK I'M GOING TO ENJOY THIS JOB.

SO WHAT MADE YOU APPLY FOR OUR YTS VACANCY, SHIRLEY?

WITH A NAME LIKE MINE, WHAT ELSE COULD I DO? BESIDES, I'VE ALWAYS WANTED TO BE A PRIVATE DETECTIVE EVER SINCE I WORKED OUT THAT MUM AND THE TOOTH FAIRY WERE ONE AND THE SAME PERSON. I RECKONED I WAS A BORN SLEUTH AFTER THAT.

Soon after . . .

SO WHAT'S OUR FIRST BIG CASE, JEFF? DIAMOND SMUGGLERS, INTERNATIONAL ART THIEVES, GOLD BULLION ROBBERS?

A MISSING DOG. I TOOK THE DETAILS OVER THE PHONE THIS MORNING. THIS IS WHERE THE CLIENT LIVES — NUMBER 24 BASKA VILLAS.

HMM. SEARCHING FOR A MISSING DOG ISN'T EXACTLY THE GLAMOROUS CAREER START I HAD IN MIND. STILL, WITH JEFF TO KEEP ME COMPANY, WHO'S COMPLAINING?

A few minutes later . . .

SO WHEN DID YOU LAST SEE YOUR DOG, MRS BUTLER?

THREE O'CLOCK YESTERDAY AFTERNOON. ONE MINUTE HE WAS PLAYING IN THE BACK YARD, THE NEXT MINUTE HE WAS GONE. VANISHED INTO THIN AIR.

IT'S ALL RIGHT, MRS BUTLER, I'M SEARCHING FOR CLUES. I SEE FROM ALL THE HAIR ON THESE COVERS THAT YOUR DOG LIKED SITTING IN THIS CHAIR.

EM . . . HAVE YOU LOST SOMETHING, DEAR? I'M ALWAYS DROPPING THINGS BETWEEN THE CUSHIONS OF THE SETTEE.

SO DOES MR BUTLER. MY HUSBAND'S BEEN GOING VERY BALD LATELY. IT'S MADE HIM EXTREMELY SHORT-TEMPERED. HAVING TO FIGHT THE DOG FOR HIS FAVOURITE CHAIR HASN'T HELPED THINGS, EITHER.

HMM. I SHOULD SAY AT A ROUGH GUESS THAT YOUR DOG IS A 14-YEAR-OLD MONGREL TERRIER, OF UNTIDY APPEARANCE, PRONE TO FLEAS, WITH A WEAK LEFT EYE AND A PRONOUNCED LIMP.

HEAVENS! THAT'S MORIARTY TO A TEE! YOU MUST BE VERY CLEVER TO HAVE WORKED ALL THAT OUT FROM A SINGLE HAIR. I'M AMAZED! I WAS OBVIOUSLY RIGHT TO GIVE THE CASE TO YOUR FIRM.

OH ... EM ... YES, MRS BUTLER. SHIRLEY HERE IS ONE OF OUR TOP OPERATIVES. IF ANYONE CAN FIND MORIARTY, SHE CAN. ANYHOW, WE WON'T TAKE UP ANY MORE OF YOUR TIME. COME ON, SHIRLEY, LET'S MAKE TRACKS.

Outside ...

YOU WERE FANTASTIC IN THERE, SHIRLEY. I'VE NEVER SEEN ANYTHING LIKE IT. ALL THAT INFORMATION FROM JUST ONE DOG HAIR. HOW DID YOU DO IT?

SIMPLE OBSERVATION, JEFF — I HAD A PEEK AT THE FILE WHILE YOU WEREN'T LOOKING ...

YOU CRAFTY SO-AND-SO!

WELL, SHIRLEY—ANY IDEAS ON THE CASE SO FAR?

IT'S OPEN AND SHUT, IF YOU ASK ME. THE HUSBAND DIDN'T LIKE THE DOG NICKING HIS FAVOURITE CHAIR SO HE GOT RID OF THE POOR OLD MUTT. SIMPLE AS THAT. AFTER ALL, IT'S ALWAYS A BUTLER THAT DUNNIT, INNIT?

GROAN! I HOPE YOUR POWERS OF DETECTION ARE BETTER THAN YOUR JOKES. THAT ONE CERTAINLY NEEDS THE KISS OF LIFE!

Soon after ...

WHAT NOW, JEFF?

THIS IS WHAT WE CALL A STAKE-OUT, SHIRLEY.

GREAT! I WONDERED WHEN LUNCH WAS. I'M FAMISHED! CAN I HAVE CHIPS AND ONIONS WITH MINE!

IT'S NOT A TAKE-AWAY, YOU CLOWN — WE'RE WATCHING SOMEONE'S PREMISES. IN THIS CASE, THE LOCAL PET SHOP.

IT'S ALWAYS POSSIBLE THAT SOMEONE MIGHT FIND MORIARTY AND TRY TO SELL HIM TO A LOCAL PET SHOP. WE HAVE TO EXPLORE EVERY AVENUE.

But ...

WE'VE BEEN HERE TWO HOURS AND NOTHING'S HAPPENED. APART FROM YOUR LEG GOING TO SLEEP, THAT IS. I RECKON IT'S TIME WE MOVED IN AND ASKED A FEW QUESTIONS. DO YOU FANCY HAVING A GO?

LEAVE IT TO ME. I'LL BE REALLY DISCREET.

And ...

YES? CAN I HELP YOU?

I'LL HAVE TO BE CAREFUL HERE. I DON'T WANT TO GIVE ANYTHING AWAY. SHE MAY HAVE POOR OLD MORIARTY TIED UP IN A KENNEL OUT THE BACK. SHE LOOKS THE SORT.

YES ... EM ... I'M LOOKING FOR A DOG. NOTHING SPECIAL. SAY ... EM ... ABOUT 14-YEARS-OLD, MONGREL, BIT SHABBY, FLEA-INFESTED, WEAK LEFT EYE AND A WONKY BACK LEG. I EXPECT YOU'VE GOT SOMETHING LIKE THAT, HAVE YOU?

HOW DARE YOU! THE ONLY THING YOU'LL GET FROM ME IS THE BACK OF MY HAND IF YOU COME IN HERE AGAIN. WHAT SORT OF ESTABLISHMENT DO YOU THINK THIS IS? WE SELL ONLY THE FINEST PEDIGREE PUPPIES HERE. GO ON, CLEAR OFF OR I'LL CALL THE POLICE!

I ONLY ASKED ...

Outside ...

WHAT HAPPENED, THEN?

HIGHLY SUSPICIOUS IF YOU ASK ME, JEFF. AS SOON AS I GAVE HER MORIARTY'S DESCRIPTION SHE CHUCKED ME OUT. SHE'S DEFINITELY GOT SOMETHING TO HIDE. I RECKON YOU SHOULD GO IN NOW AND GET THE CUFFS ON HER. I'LL WAIT IN THE CAR IN CASE IT TURNS NASTY.

THANKS A LOT.

WHAT ARE YOU DOING NOW?

I HAVE TO MAKE A PHONECALL.

THIS IS NO TIME FOR IDLE CHIT-CHAT, JEFF. MORIARTY COULD BE IN TERRIBLE DANGER.

I DOUBT IT, SOMEHOW. BESIDES, I HAVE TO PHONE MR BAKER EVERY TWO HOURS. HE LIKES TO BE KEPT UP-TO-DATE ON OUR PROGRESS. KEEP AN EYE ON THE CAR. THIS IS A ROUGH NEIGHBOURHOOD. THEY'LL MAKE OFF WITH THE TYRES GIVEN HALF A CHANCE.

A few minutes later . . .

WHAT'S WRONG, SHIRLEY?

IT'S THE TYRES, JEFF — SOMEONE'S STOLEN THEM.

OH, NO! I TOLD YOU TO KEEP AN EYE ON THEM. MR BAKER WILL GO WILD! THEY COST TWENTY QUID EACH!

THAT'S NOT THE WORST OF IT, THOUGH.

IT ISN'T?

THEY'RE STILL ATTACHED TO THE CAR!

OH, NO! MR BAKER'LL HAVE OUR GUTS FOR GARTERS. DID YOU GET THEIR DESCRIPTION?

NO. BUT I GOT THEIR NUMBER!

AAGH!

DID I DO SOMETHING WRONG, THEN?

While Jeff rang the police . . .

A GOOD DETECTIVE IS ALWAYS ON THE LOOK-OUT FOR CLUES. DOGS OFTEN RUB THEMSELVES UP AGAINST LAMP-POSTS AND THINGS. PERHAPS MORIARTY CAME THIS WAY AND LEFT SOME TELL-TALE SIGNS. IT'S WORTH A TRY.

YOU POOR DEAR. YOUR EYESIGHT'S WORSE THAN MINE. THAT MAGNIFYING GLASS IS NO SUBSTITUTE FOR A GOOD PAIR OF GLASSES, YOU KNOW. LET ME HELP YOU ACROSS THE ROAD.

NO, REALLY, THERE'S NO NEED—

IT'S NO TROUBLE AT ALL, MY DEAR . . .

Then . . .

THAT DOG MATCHES MORIARTY'S DESCRIPTION! THERE'S NO TIME TO CALL JEFF. I'LL HAVE TO TACKLE THIS ON MY OWN. IF I CAN CLEAR UP THE CASE PROMPTLY, MAYBE MR BAKER WON'T SACK ME. I'M REALLY CUT OUT FOR THIS DETECTIVE WORK — I'D HATE TO LOSE THE JOB.

A TRUE DETECTIVE IS A MASTER OF A THOUSAND DISGUISES, ABLE TO MERGE IN WITH ANY SURROUNDINGS. SHE'LL NEVER SUSPECT THAT I'M FOLLOWING HER. HMM. THAT'S MORIARTY, ALL RIGHT. I'M SURE OF IT. IT'S TIME I MADE A CITIZEN'S ARREST.

THAT'S FAR ENOUGH, MADAM!

WHAT?

HOLD IT RIGHT THERE, MISS!

WHAT?

THIS LOOKS LIKE A CLEAR CASE OF ATTEMPTED PICK-POCKETING TO ME. LET'S HAVE A FEW DETAILS. NAME AND ADDRESS, PLEASE.

IT'S ALL RIGHT, OFFICER, I'M A PRIVATE DETECTIVE. MY NAME IS HOLMES.

OH, YES — SHERLOCK HOLMES, WOULD THAT BE, THEN?

OF COURSE NOT. WHAT SORT OF NAME IS THAT FOR A GIRL? MY NAME'S SHIRLEY.

AND WHERE'S DR WATSON, THEN? AT HOME IN BAKER STREET?

NO. HE'S ROUND THE CORNER, MAKING A PHONECALL. NOT THAT HE'S A DOCTOR, OF COURSE. HE'S A PRIVATE DETECTIVE, TOO — JUST LIKE ME. HE'LL EXPLAIN EVERYTHING.

OF COURSE HE WILL. HE CAN MEET US LATER DOWN AT THE POLICE STATION. WE'VE GOT OUR OWN DOCTOR THERE. HE'LL TAKE A LOOK AT YOU. NOW IF YOU'LL JUST COME QUIETLY . . .

IT'S ALL RIGHT, MADAM. THE POOR GIRL'S OBVIOUSLY SUFFERING FROM DELUSIONS. SHE'S NOT RESPONSIBLE FOR HER ACTIONS. WE'LL MAKE SURE SHE'S LOOKED AFTER DOWN AT THE STATION.

YOU THINK I'M MAD, DON'T YOU? BUT I'M NOT! I'M NOT EVEN A LITTLE BIT ANGRY. BUT I WILL BE IF YOU DON'T LET ME GO RIGHT NOW! HELP! POLICE! OH! WHAT AM I SAYING?

Some time later . . .

THANKS FOR SPRINGING ME, JEFF. I SUPPOSE I HAVE TO LIE LOW FOR A FEW DAYS NOW, DO I?

YOU WILL WHEN MR BAKER HEARS ABOUT THIS. HE LIKES TO KEEP ON GOOD TERMS WITH THE POLICE. HE WON'T TAKE TOO KINDLY TO ONE OF HIS OPERATIVES BEING ARRESTED ON HER FIRST CASE.

Back at the office . . .

WELL? IS IT BACK TO THE JOB CENTRE FOR ME, THEN?

NO. AFTER I RANG, THE GUYS WHO PINCHED OUR CAR WERE CAUGHT TWO STREETS AWAY. THEY WERE PART OF A GANG THE POLICE HAVE BEEN TRYING TO NAB FOR MONTHS. MR BAKER'S A WILY OLD SO-AND-SO. HE CONVINCED THE LOCAL INSPECTOR THAT IT WAS ALL PART OF A PLAN HE'D SET UP. HE'S FLAVOUR OF THE MONTH WITH THEM NOW. AND THAT MEANS WE'RE IN THE CLEAR, TOO.

SO WE'RE BACK ON THE CASE OF THE MISSING DOG, THEN?

NOT QUITE. APPARENTLY, TWO MINUTES AFTER WE LEFT MRS BUTLER THIS MORNING, MORIARTY NIPPED BACK OVER THE GARDEN FENCE, NONE THE WORSE FOR WEAR.

THAT'S ABOUT THE SIZE OF IT.

YOU MEAN WE'VE BEEN ON A WILD-DOG-CHASE ALL DAY LONG?

SO WHERE DOES THAT LEAVE US, NOW?

ANOTHER STAKE-OUT.

OH, NO! DO WE HAVE TO? WHERE IS IT THIS TIME?

A NICE LITTLE RESTAURANT JUST DOWN THE ROAD. AND THIS TIME YOU CAN HAVE ALL THE CHIPS AND ONIONS YOU WANT. THEN WE CAN GET DOWN TO SOME REAL DETECTIVE WORK. AFTER ALL, IF WE'RE GOING TO WORK TOGETHER FROM NOW ON, WE SHOULD GET TO KNOW EACH OTHER A LITTLE BETTER, DON'T YOU THINK?

YOU KNOW, I THINK I COULD TAKE TO THIS PRIVATE DETECTIVE LARK AFTER ALL. IT'S NOT THAT DIFFICULT WHEN YOU GET DOWN TO IT, IS IT, JEFF?

NOT REALLY, SHIRLEY. IN FACT, IT'S ALL RATHER SIMPLE. ONE MIGHT EVEN SAY, ELEMENTARY, MY DEAR HOLMES. ELEMENTARY . . .

THE END

This foxy chick -sportin' the latest designer net curtains is Sandie Shaw who won the Eurovision Song Contest in 1967 with "Puppet On A String". She also had a penchant for walking about barefoot all the time . . .

Guess who? She had a major hit with the Pet Shop Boys a while back and is famous for her very tasteful thick black eye make-up. Yes, it's the lovely Dusty Springfield.

Yes . . . well . . . we're not altogether sure what the Blue Peter gang are doing with handfuls of cutlery either!

FASHION

At the beginning of the decade the fashions were pretty much the same as the Fifties. Men wore suits and tight jeans and women wore sheath dresses, swirly skirts and "winkle-picker" shoes. But by about 1963 the style of the Sixties had begun to emerge. Clothes became less restricted. Dresses were unwaisted and almost childlike. Trouser suits for women were very popular, worn with hideous flowery blouses with shoulder-duster collars — bleurgh! White rubber calf-length boots appeared as did the infamous Chelsea boot and PVC mac. Mary Quant invented the mini-skirt which got shorter and shorter to the point of just covering a bottom and no more!

The ideal shape for both men and women was skinny and boyish.

By 1969 the hippy cult was at its height as were kaftans, cheesecloth shirts, headscarves and Afghan coats!

This was also the age of the "boutique" and places like Carnaby Street, Chelsea and the King's Road were very trendy. The design houses of the time were pretty much as they are today with Christian Dior and Yves St. Laurent at the top of the scale. Biba and Mary Quant catered for the ready-to-wear look preferred by the young trendies.

MUSIC

For many the music is what makes the Sixties memorable. Some of it was pretty weird, a bit of it was pretty drastic but most of it was brilliant!

There were bands with stupid names, heart-throbs like Elvis Presley (whose gyrating pelvis and provocative pout caused a veritable storm of protest!) and many legends such as The Beatles, The Rolling Stones, Marvin Gaye, The Kinks and The Supremes to name but a few.

There was a great mixture of music throughout the decade. At the beginning there were plenty of rock 'n' roll and boppy tunes. Then, in about 1963, soul music became predominant in the charts. In the latter part of the decade, along with the flower power cult, CND and women's liberation movements, came hippy music from bands like The Doors and Procol Harem.

There were many many classic singles released in those days — many of which are still played on the radio and heard in discos throughout the world.

CLASSIC SIXTIES HITS

"My Girl" — The Temptations
"Light My Fire" — The Doors
"My Generation" — The Who
"Summer Holiday" — Cliff Richard
"Hard Day's Night" — The Beatles
"Shout!" — Lulu
"In The Ghetto" — Elvis Presley
"That'll Be The Day" — The Everly Brothers
"Waterloo Sunset" — The Kinks
"The Sun Ain't Gonna Shine Any More"
— The Walker Brothers
"She's Not There" — The Zombies

A FEW BAD ONES
"Two Little Boys" — Rolf Harris
"Ob-La-Di Ob-La-Da" — Marmalade
"Chirpy Chirpy Cheep Cheep"
— Middle Of The Road
"Come Outside" — Mike Sarnes and Wendy Richards

ENTERTAINMENT

Up until the Sixties, television sets had been fairly few and far between but as they became more advanced they got cheaper and were soon available to everyone. At this time, most of the BJ gang were widdle kiddies so we really only remember things like 'Andy Pandy' and 'Looby Lou',

EVER HEARD YOUR PARENTS DRONING ON ABOUT "THE GOOD 'OLE DAYS"? WELL, HERE'S YOUR CHANCE TO FIND OUT WHAT THEY WERE REALLY LIKE!

THE 60's

The Daleks — many a Sixties' kid (that includes most of the BJ gang) hid behind the sofa when this nasty bunch came on the telly at teatime on Saturdays.

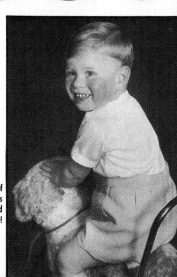

The Sixties was the heyday of really bad, bad horror films, like the Hammer productions, and were always about the occult, Dracula or werewolves like this one starring the young Oliver Reed.

The Duke of York — he was a chubby lad even then!

but slightly older members of the office (namely The Ed!) remember classics like 'Joe 90' and the 'Thunderbirds' first time round! All the best children's programmes were made in the Sixties — 'The Herbs', 'Hector's House', 'Hickory House' and 'The Magic Roundabout' are among the top favourites.

This was the decade when music programmes started to appear on the box — 'Ready Steady Go!', 'Juke Box Jury' and 'Top of The Pops' all started life in the Sixties. Radio One first hit the airwaves in 1967 with DJs such as John Peel and Jimmy Savile who're still going strong.

There were loads of cult TV shows such as 'The Man From U.N.C.L.E.', 'The Monkees', 'The Prisoner', 'The Champions', 'Hogan's Heroes', the dashing 'Dr Kildare' and 'Star Trek' to name a few!

This was also the time when the "very bad horror movie" was invented. They were usually about little green men from Mars, space travel, werewolves or Dracula. The Hammer House of Horror was responsible for the majority of these which are good for a laugh if nothing else!

There were tons of movies around then. A lot were pretty strange but then so are a lot of today's movies! Many a famous person made a name for themselves back then, for example, Dustin Hoffman, Paul Newman, Elizabeth Taylor, Robert Redford, Brigitte Bardot, Jane Fonda, Racquel Welch, Terence Stamp, Oliver Reed.

CLASSIC SIXTIES FILMS
'Psycho'
'The Hustler'
'The Graduate'
'The Sound Of Music'
'The Good, The Bad And The Ugly'
'Goldfinger'
'Lawrence Of Arabia'
'Alfie'

EVENTS

The Sixties were pretty much an event in themselves if you think about it! There were all sorts of wondrous things going on! Space travel was possibly the most exciting! In the space (har! har!) of a mere ten years man travelled around the moon, space-walked and landed on the moon — not bad eh?

The most famous hippy festival of all time took place in 1967 at Woodstock, somewhere in America. The Great Train Robbery, which is *still* being discussed on the news, took place in the early part of the decade. The Mini (as in the car) was invented and colour came to TV screens all over the world.

In 1963, President of the USA, John F. Kennedy, who's wife was apparently the most beautiful woman in the world, was assassinated in Dallas.

Several other wondrous people died in those years — Clark Gable, Marilyn Monroe, Eddie Cochran, Sam Cooke, Otis Redding, Stan Laurel, Boris Karloff and Martin Luther King.

However, Prince Andrew, Prince Edward and most of the BJ gang were born then — aren't you glad?!

The Beatles falling from the top of a building . . . Well, maybe it's just trick photography or somefink?!

'The Magic Roundabout', a wonderful kiddies' programme which most of the BJ gang grew up with. Zebedee was the undisputed favourite!

Mary Quant — infamous inventor of the mini-skirt which drove men to distraction!

Many a young lass longed for Twiggy's childlike figure, big eyes and innocent looks. However, we, the BJ gang, think this type of figure is most unattractive!

'Joe 90', the cult children's television show of the Sixties, created by Gerry Anderson who also created such timeless classics as the 'Thunderbirds' and 'Fireball XL 5'.

Secret Agent Ilya Kuryakin (David McCallum) star of the grown-up cult series 'The Man From U.N.C.L.E.'. (Kindly stop drooling, girls! — The Ed.)

Is any member of this rather suspect group a parent of yours? If so, disown them — NOW!!

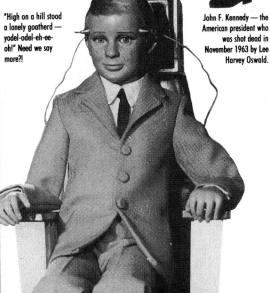

"High on a hill stood a lonely goatherd — yodel-odel-eh-ee-oh!" Need we say more?!

John F. Kennedy — the American president who was shot dead in November 1963 by Lee Harvey Oswald.

WHO SC

THOUSANDS of people all over the world suffer from unreasonable fears — commonly known as phobias. Some are afraid to leave the house, others hate being in a closed space.

To those of us who don't suffer from these fears their reactions might seem a bit over the top but for them it's only too real.

Some of us flip our lids at the sight of spiders or rats while others feel faint at the mere mention of something as seemingly harmless as a teapot or twig! Phobias have been around for a long, long time. Elizabeth I had a great fear of roses, Sigmund Freud, the psychologist, was phobic about travel, Edward VII was terrified of the number 13 and apparently a famous Fleet Street-er, Dr Johnson, always performed a little jig on the front doorstep of his house before going in! Some people have to wash their hands before and after they do anything, others pull out every plug in the house and then double check before they go out!

However, suffering from such little habits and obsessions doesn't mean you're mad!

Many a psychologist has researched this most interesting subject and they've come to the conclusion that more often than not they are symbolic of some little problem or anxiety. For example, a fear of crossing bridges seems to have something to do with not being able to make decisions. Y'know, like whether to dye your hair or perm it!

The theory behind phobias goes summatt like this . . .

Whenever you're in an unpleasant situation and you become scared, things that are around at that time become objects of fear. Say, for example, you suddenly panic about something while you're watching an episode of 'EastEnders', you may well cower and cringe for some time after, every time you see a picture of Lofty Holloway!

According to Norman Lee, an authority on the subject, the things that make us come out in a cold sweat are called "triggers". He reckoned that about 4½ million of us have these weird triggers — spook!!

Common Phobias — (or "triggers" if you want to be intellectual about it.)

Injections — well, let's be honest, is there anyone out there who actually enjoys them?! Some people, though, need to be chained down and blindfolded before they'll face a needle!

Moths — the sound and sight of soft, hairy wings flapping has been known to reduce our tough Editor to a quivering wreck!

Parties — a fear of being bored by some creep's life history?

Dentists — this affects the entire human race — if it doesn't affect you there's something wrong!

Lifts — a fear of being stuck with your own company for more than ten minutes.

Snakes — this often affects people who've never even seen a live one before!

Blushing — y'know the sort of thing — as soon as someone says you're blushing, even though you don't know you are, you more than likely start blushing just because you're thinking about it — understand?!

Spiders — there are so many different fears associated with this that we'd have to work during lunch time to write them out so we're not going to bother!

Heights — again, there are about six million different reasons for this phobia so we'll just give you the most obvious — fear of falling?!

Thunder — even some of the most grown-up adults we know (not mentioning any names in particular!) hide under the nearest desk at the hint of a rumble from the skies above!

Rats and Mice — speaks for itself, really . . . eeuugh!!

40

FOR SOME PEOPLE IT'S THINGS THAT GO BUMP IN THE NIGHT THAT GIVES THEM THE COLLY-WOBBLES, OTHERS GET THE HEEBEE-GEEBEES AT THE SIGHT OF TOE-NAIL CLIPPINGS. WHAT TURNS YOU TO JELLY?

ARES WINS!

This subject has sparked off many an interesting discussion here in BJ towers. In fact, we've brightened up several dull and boring hours and consumed gallons of canteen coffee in an effort to get to the bottom of our own phobias!

Andrea — "Polystyrene is most definitely my phobia — even the thought of the squeaky noise it makes when someone rubs it sends shivers down my spine!"

Allyson — "I'm terrified of heights — being any higher than three feet off the ground makes me feel sick — I can't even go up a step ladder!" That's just an excuse for not cleaning the BJ office windows!

Val — "The thought of being smothered terrifies me — I suppose I must be claustrophobic . . ."

Lesley — "I hate the way Fiona bites her cutlery when she's eating — it's almost the same as someone scraping their nail down a blackboard!" (Shrieks from the BJ gang!)

Karen — It appears that Karen has a phobia about just about everything — you name it, she's scared of it!

The Ed — "Moths and nylon bring me out in a cold sweat, tears, the shivers, etc., etc. . . .!" (Aww, maybe she's not quite the old battleaxe she pretends to be!)

Ali — for some reason, unknown to us, Ali's terrified of being trapped under a bed . . .!?!

Morag — "For as long as I can remember wasps (and other flying things) have been my biggest fear. If there's one within a mile radius of me, I go mental! The worst thing is whenever you run away, they follow. Nasty little creatures!"

Fiona — "I hate anything supernatural. I hate ghost stories, spooky movies and anything else remotely scary!"

Nikki — "I'm the same as Morag — anything that buzzes, stings and flies turns me into a quivering wreck. Last summer, I was often seen screaming down the hallowed BJ corridors with a big fat bumble bee or a long skinny wasp in hot pursuit!"

Annie Lennox used to be frightened of crowds. She must be used to it by now, though!

Boy George has a fear of getting old. (It comes to us all, George, it comes to us all — words of wisdom from The Ed.)

Westworld drummer, **Nick Burton,** has an inexplicable pathological hatred of celery. Could it be because of the stringy bits that get stuck in your teeth . . .?!

No matter what your phobia is you won't be alone — there's bound to be someone somewhere in the world that's as terrified of earwigs as you are!

41

TOP TEN WORST FEARS OF THE BRITISH PUBLIC.

1. Public speaking
2. Heights
3. Insects and bugs
4. Debt
5. Deep Water
6. Sickness
7. Death
8. Flying
9. Loneliness
10. Dogs

If you didn't have any fears before you read this you probably do now! But don't worry, we're told all phobias are curable!!

The hotel plants were watered every Monday, a very special day for Karen.

LOVE GROWS!

THERE'S COLIN AGAIN! ISN'T HE FANTASTIC?

WELL, WHY DON'T YOU CHAT HIM UP? HE'S ALWAYS WATCHING YOU — I BET HE'S DYING TO SPEAK.

I WISH I COULD, BUT I SEEM TO GET ALL TONGUE-TIED AS SOON AS I'M NEAR HIM.

COULDN'T YOU COMPLIMENT HIM ON HIS PLANTS OR SOMETHING?

ME? I DON'T KNOW A DAISY FROM A DAHLIA . . . MIND YOU, IT MIGHT BE WORTH SWOTTING UP ON THE SUBJECT . . .

So . . .

WHAT ON EARTH HAVE YOU GOT THERE, KAREN?

GARDENING BOOKS! I'VE JUST BEEN TO THE LIBRARY. I'M GOING TO BECOME A PLANT EXPERT AND IMPRESS COLIN WITH MY KNOWLEDGE!

YOU MUST HAVE CLEARED OUT THE SHELVES!

I'LL NEVER GET THESE LATIN NAMES RIGHT. THEY'RE SO COMPLICATED! JACOBINIA CARNEA . . . AND THIS ONE . . . NOTACACTUS LENINGHAUSII . . .

SOUNDS LIKE A DISEASE.

WELL, I HOPE ALL YOUR HARD WORK PAYS OFF, KAREN.

The next Monday Karen was ready for action . . .

HI, THERE! THAT'S A HEPHROLEPIS EXALTATA, ISN'T IT? NEEDS A BIT OF PERKING UP, DOESN'T IT?

WHAT? OH, YES, IT DEFINITELY NEEDS A BIT OF ATTENTION.

I LOVE PLANTS. GLORIOSA ROTHSCHILDIANA IS ONE OF MY FAVOURITES. DON'T YOU THINK IT'S BEAUTIFUL?

OH — OH, YES, I DO. IT'S ONE OF MY FAVOURITES, TOO.

And it appeared her plan had worked . . .

YOU KNOW, IT'S GREAT TO MEET A GIRL WHO SHARES MY INTEREST IN PLANTS. SOME PEOPLE JUST COULDN'T CARE LESS ABOUT THEM.

OH, I . . . I THINK PLANTS ARE WONDERFUL.

IN THAT CASE, WOULD YOU LIKE TO COME WITH ME TO THE NEW GARDEN CENTRE THAT'S OPENING IN TOWN THIS WEEKEND? I'VE JUST NOTICED IT ADVERTISED IN THE PAPER.

THAT'S A WONDERFUL IDEA. I'D LOVE TO, COLIN.

RIGHT, I'LL SEE YOU SATURDAY, THEN!

GREAT! AND WE CAN COMPARE NOTES ON THE PLANTS THEY'VE GOT IN STOCK.

So the pretence wasn't over yet . . .

LOOKS LIKE I'D BETTER KEEP UP THE PLANT STUDIES! OTHERWISE COLIN'LL FIND OUT I'VE BEEN LYING TO HIM.

And on Saturday Karen had more than one reason for being nervous . . .

I'M SURE I'LL NEVER RECOGNISE ANY OF THESE PLANTS.

HI, KAREN. WHAT'S THIS, CATCHING UP ON SOME READING?

OH . . . EM . . . IT'S JUST A SPECIALIST BOOK I'VE BEEN AFTER FOR AGES . . .

THIS IS IMPRESSIVE. I MUST SAY, IT SEEMS TO BE STOCKED FULL OF HYBRID VARIETIES . . . OF COURSE, I DON'T NEED TO TELL YOU WHAT THEY ALL ARE, DO I?

EM . . . NO. BUT THEY ALL LOOK VERY HEALTHY, DON'T THEY?

THIS ONE LOOKS REALLY SPECIAL, DOESN'T IT? MUST BE A NEW VARIETY. HAVE YOU ANY IDEA WHICH?

NO, ACTUALLY . . . I'VE NEVER SEEN IT BEFORE.

OH, OH . . . I KNEW IT HAD TO HAPPEN. I DON'T HAVE A CLUE WHAT IT IS.

EM . . . I WAS HOPING TO SEE SOME PLATYCERIUM ALICORNE . . . YOU HAVEN'T SEEN ANY, HAVE YOU?

NO, NOT SO FAR, ANYWAY.

Before they left . . .

I'D LIKE YOU TO HAVE THIS, KAREN. A MEMENTO OF OUR FIRST DATE. YOU KNOW WHAT IT IS, DON'T YOU?

I . . . EM . . . ACTUALLY THE NAME ESCAPES ME . . . IT'S ON THE TIP OF MY TONGUE . . .

OH, IT'S NO GOOD . . . WHAT IS IT, NOW?

WHAT IS IT . . . OH . . . EM . . . IT'S MULTIFLORUS DREADICOSPULUM, OF COURSE.

OH, OF COURSE, SILLY OF ME TO FORGET.

So . . .

SEE YOU MONDAY AT THE HOTEL! MAYBE WE CAN ARRANGE A VISIT TO ONE OF THE HORTICULTURAL SHOWS NEXT WEEKEND.

OH, COLIN, I'LL LOOK FORWARD TO THAT.

OH, FOR A VISIT TO A NICE, UNCOMPLICATED DISCO!

On Monday morning . . .

HI, KAREN. HOW DID THE DATE WITH COLIN GO?

IT WAS GREAT . . . EXCEPT THAT I HAD A BIG STRUGGLE TO KEEP UP THE PRETENCE OF BEING A PLANT EXPERT.

I SEE YOU'RE STILL STUDYING THEM?

I'VE BOUGHT COLIN A LITTLE CACTUS IN RETURN FOR THIS PLANT HE GAVE ME. IT'S REALLY SPECIAL . . . IT'S A MULTIFLORUS DREADICOSPULUM.

A MULTI-WHAT? IT LOOKS JUST LIKE A BUSY LIZZIE TO ME!

IT DOES, DOESN'T IT? MY MUM'S GOT ONE JUST LIKE IT IN HER KITCHEN.

COLIN DEFINITELY SAID IT WAS A MULTIFLORUS DREADICOSPULUM.

BUT IT SAYS IN HERE THAT THE LATIN NAME FOR A BUSY LIZZIE IS IMPATIENS WALLERIANA.

I TOLD YOU IT WAS SPECIAL. IT CAN'T BE A BUSY LIZZIE.

BUT THERE ISN'T ANY SUCH NAME AS MULTIFLORUS DREADICOSPULUM IN THIS BOOK.

PERHAPS IT'S SO SPECIAL THEY HAVEN'T GOT ITS NAME IN ANY REFERENCE BOOKS YET.

THE END

John Travolta struts his funky thang at the local disco.

BLEE! The 'look' every young girly wanted in the 70's.

Swap Shop — a massive TV hit even though its toothy presenters favoured smock tops and kipper ties.

POP

Females seemed to be going completely wiggy over Donny Osmond and David Cassidy at the beginning of the 70's. One of these dreamboats only had to raise an eyebrow and girls would faint all over the place. With hits such as "Puppy Love" and "I Write The Songs" Dave 'n' Donny were not exactly stompin' rawkers from hell, but nevertheless they could do absolutely no wrong as far as teenage Britain was concerned. The Bay City Rollers came along a bit later and the nation dropped the American popstars like hot bricks and rushed out to the shops to snap up tartan trimmed flares and tank tops. These were the blee-togs that every truly loyal fan of the band had to have. In 1974 Abba won the Eurovision Song Contest with "Waterloo" and by the end of the decade had an astonishing 17 top ten singles under their belts. Their runaway success prompted other dodgy foreign people to record the same sort of happy-go-lucky pop records and Boney M crashed onto the scene with such 'deep 'n' meaningful' ditties as "Hooray Hooray It's A Holi-holiday" and "Ma Baker". From 1975 onwards disco fever seemed to take over. With the release of the "Saturday Night Fever" album the whole population of Britain seemed to spend their time wiggling their bottoms, sticking their index fingers in the air and generally frugging rather wildly to the funky disco beat. It wasn't until the Punk explosion in 1976 that things started getting raunchy; but as they say, that's another story.

Other stompin' 70's rockers — Gary Glitter Mud, Sailor, The Boomtown Rats, The Sex Pistols, David Bowie.

FASHION

There were certainly a lot of dreamy fashion 'looks' in the 70's. Everything seemed to be, er, 'voluminous'. Flares were ginormous, and collars were simply gigantic. What's more, shoes weren't in the slightest bit fashionable unless they had three inch platforms on them, which made for a lot of accidents when people tried to run for the bus. If they didn't trip on their billowing trousers they'd almost certainly topple over in their wedged sandals, or be blinded by a fly-away collar flapping in the wind. No, sirree, practicality was not the name of the game in the 70's. By the end of the decade Olivia Newton John had rocked the fashion world in the film 'Grease' and soon every trendy youngster in the world had a pair of skin-tight lycra trews and a spangly boob tube. Hairstyles were also truly horrific and the 'long straggly' look favoured by most females at the beginning of the decade soon (literally) got the chop when the revolutionary 'page-boy' cut came along. Then Joanna Lumley appeared and the hair-do she favoured in the TV series 'The New Avengers' was all the rage. 'The Purdie' as it was known really seemed to be a variation on the bowl cut, but that didn't stop everyone wanting the look.

Other fashion crazes of the 70's — kaftans, catsuits, 'skinny-rib' polo necks, bin bags.

TV AND FILMS

Those square-eyed people amongst us certainly had a lot to goggle at in the 70s. There were some truly awful TV programmes like 'The Generation Game' which was on every Saturday night for absolute yonks. Every week the audience would gasp at the hostess Anthea Redfern's frocks (go on, give us a twirl, give us a twirl) and squirm in their seats as some poor contestant tried to run off a never-ending list of conveyer belt goodies. Bruce Forsyth and his chin were followed later on in the evening by 'Starsky And Hutch' who were considered v. 'hunky fellas' indeed. 'Swap Shop' revolutionised boring Saturday mornings for kids

BORN TOO LATE TO HAVE BEEN ABLE TO FULLY APPRECIATE THE SUMPTUOUS 70's? WELL READERS, NEVER FEAR, WE'VE DECIDED TO SHOW YOU JUST WHAT YOU MISSED OUT ON. HOLD ON TO YOUR HATS...

THE 70's

Abba offer their fingerprints to Swedish police after being arrested for wearing illegally naff clothes.

Everyone tottered about in platforms in the 70's. Sorry you missed out, readers?

How every street-cred young girly got to the shops in the 70's. Phew, love those flares.

The barnet craze that swept the nation. Resplendent 'page boy' haircut, complete with flick. Mmm . . .

everywhere, and there were also tea-time treats like 'Rentaghost', 'Jackanory' and 'The Tomorrow People'.

In the early 70's David Cassidy starred as a member of the fictitious 'Partridge Family' — the story of a woman touring the country with her army of toothy all singin' all dancin' sprogs. Spook! One of those 'talented' youngsters was played by Susan Dey, who now stars in L.A. Law!

Film buffs had a 'beezer' time of it in the 70's. The first 'Rocky' film really packed a punch (ho, ho) in the nation's cinemas and swimming pools got deserted v. quickly indeed after 'Jaws' was released. However, no-one could possibly have predicted the success of 'Saturday Night Fever' and 'Grease' which had movie-goers returning to the cinema again and again to drool over John Travolta's swarthy hunksomeness. The sound tracks from these two 'flicks' went down a treat at the record shops too and soon everyone was trying to emulate Mr Travolta's hip-thrusts down the youth club disco. Phew, those were the days . . .

CRAZES

The 70's saw a lot of crazes come and go. Skateboards were soon causing rather a lot of congestion on the pavements of Great Britain, and all of a sudden specially built concrete carbuncles were springing up for all those skateboarders to whizz about on. That was a bit of a mistake, though, as by the time the 80's came along nobody would be seen dead on one! Another curious phenomenon was 'Slime' which school-kids everywhere used to leave in the most revolting places. Someone must have made a fortune from selling these plastic tubs full of sludge green goo, but that was OK, as Margaret Thatcher had just got into power and was advocating free enterprise for all.

A very brazen lady called Erica Roe decided during a rugby match that it would be a jolly good idea to peel off her clothes and run across the pitch. Thus the streaking craze was off to a start. Not a football match or a Royal Tour went by without someone baring their bod to the nearest camera. Ahem, moving quickly along . . . 'Moon Dust' hit the sweety shops with a bang around 1976 and soon children everywhere were making unnerving explosive noises every time they opened their mouths. This 'Moon Dust' came in little foil packets in a strange granular form and made fearful crackling noises when sucked. Goodness me, the 70's were so wacky there were simply oodles of other crazes. Too many to mention, in fact but amongst others there were clogs, space hoppers, safety pins, pogo-sticks, and . . . (Snip! We haven't got all day! — The Ed.)

The Bay City Rollers desperately try to demolish a stage by stomping all over it in big ugly platforms.

PERSONALITIES

There was a lot of scandal about in the 70's, yip, indeed there was. The President of the United States, Mr Richard Nixon, was ousted from the White House after the world was shocked by the phone tapping revelations of the Watergate affair. Top model Jerry Hall chucked her boyfriend, Bryan Ferry, and made off with his old mate, Mick Jagger and Rod Stewart and actress Britt Eckland had a rather rocky old romance which was off one minute and on the next. Bjorn Borg broke a few hearts on the centre courts of Wimbledon, and Mohammud Ali went about telling everyone he was a genius, unbeatable, and generally an all-round nice person too. Michael Parkinson, who could teach old Wogan a thing or two, interviewed absolutely everyone who was anyone on his Saturday night chat shows. The nation gasped at his antics with Rod Hull and Emu and were in cahoots over his banter with Billy

The Osmonds baring their gnashers to the nation. Do you have that Colgate ring of confidence?

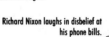

The question on everyone's lips in the late 70's — "D'ya fancy Starsky or Hutch?"

Connolly. Other personalities in the news — Noel Edmonds, John Travolta, Margaret Thatcher, Basil Brush, Harold Wilson, Mike Yarwood, Yuri Geller.

EVENTS

The Vietnam War, The Biafran Famine, Decimalisation, The Watergate Scandal, Raid on Entebbe, Princess Anne's Wedding, Sid Vicious' Suicide.

Every American mother's dream! The Partridge Family.

Richard Nixon laughs in disbelief at his phone bills.

Parky and Billy Connolly in an exchange of witty repartee.

"You can't pin this one on me!" A member of Boney M hotly denies he ever had anything to do with the band.

Bjorn Borg has a good old snog with the Wimbledon trophy. What a sport!

MORRISSEY:

Heaven knows he may be miserable, but unloveable, certainly not. A firm favourite with quite a few of the BJ office in spite of the NHS specs.

ROB LOWE:

Well what can I say, the boy's a pure dream. Glasses just add to that "little boy" look — mmmm, delicious!

BEN ELTON

Affectionately known as 'motormouth', wearing glasses has never held this man back. He was one of the writers responsible for 'The Young Ones', 'Filthy Rich and Catflap' and 'Blackadder'. Bound to be a fun guy to have around!

STING:

Bit of a sultry lad is old Sting. He's one guy perfectly entitled to wear glasses as he actually WAS a school teacher. Mind you we reckon he's sexy enough to get away with wearing *anything*.

THE PROCLAIMERS:

Although not exactly renowned for their stunning good looks, these lads do sing some funky tunes and their specs have become a 'kind of' trademark

RUPERT EVERETT:

One of the biggest names in Britain's very own Brat Pack. Rupe's a bit of a sulky boy so shades give him something to hide behind when he can't bear to face the world!

GEORGE MICHAEL:

Mr Cool. This guy is such a poser that specs are just another prop for him to play about with.

HARRISON FORD:

Famous for his role as Indiana Jones, this guy's for you if you're into older men. Glasses certainly

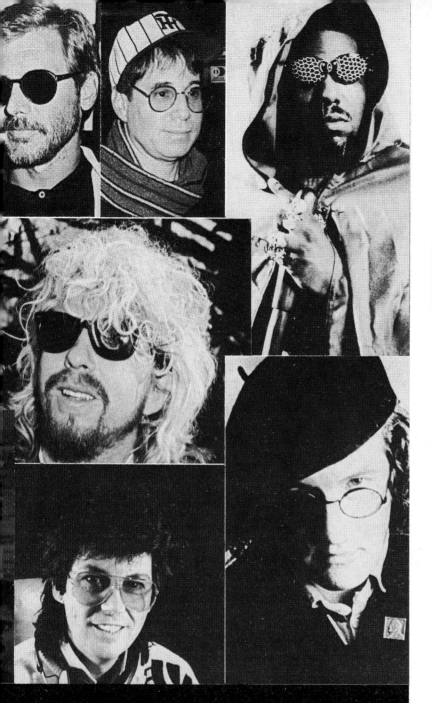

SPECS APPEAL! ⁴⁹

● Gone are the days when the only people seen dead wearing specs were school teachers and librarians. Today glasses no longer have the frumpy, old-fashioned image they used to. So feast your bifocals on these guys and dare to deny that they're worth a second glance.

We reckon that these men prove once and for all that you can be sexy, swoonsome, hunky, loveable AND still wear specs.

don't spoil his mature good looks. Not so sure about the designer stubble, though!

DAVE STEWART
I've never seen this guy without his specs. But Siobhan from Bananarama doesn't seem to mind them!

BILLY IDOL
Even when he's wearing specs Billy could never be less than a man.

MIKE REID
Famous for his 'Hey, don't I look like Cliff Richard?' impersonation, this guy could never be cool, with or without specs!

PAUL SIMON
Maybe not Mr Hunk but he did write some nice tunes back in the olden days and he might appeal to those fond of a more wimpy man.

AFRICA BAMBAATAA
Ahem, well the man's obviously got a thing about Darth Vader.

CAPTAIN SENSIBLE
This guy's definitely a bit weird (in spite of the name). Mind you I have to admit he looks kind of cute in his Lennon-type specs.

Making Plans For Nigel

The first time it happened, I just laughed it off . . .

HEY, SOPHIE — YOU LIVE NEXT DOOR TO NIGEL FINCH, DON'T YOU? LUCKY GIRL! I BET YOU'RE ALWAYS POPPING IN TO BORROW BOWLS OF SUGAR AND PINTS OF MILK — ANY EXCUSE TO SEE HIM!

EH? ARE YOU SURE YOU'VE GOT THE RIGHT NIGEL?

YEAH, OF COURSE I HAVE. HE'S GORGEOUS!

THE LAST TIME I LOOKED AT HIM HE WAS QUITE ORDINARY-LOOKING WITH SPOTS ON HIS CHIN.

IF YOU SEE HIM, GIVE HIM MY LOVE.

THAT'S AMAZING — IMAGINE A GIRL BEING INTERESTED IN SPOTTY NIGEL. I DON'T THINK HE'S EVEN NOTICED THAT GIRLS EXIST — HE'S TOO BUSY WORKING ON THAT BIKE OF HIS.

COME ON, SOPHIE, HE'S NOT THAT BAD. I THINK NIGEL'S QUITE CUTE.

The second time it happened I was mildly amused . . .

OH, SOPHIE, I'M GLAD I'VE SEEN YOU. YOU LIVE NEXT DOOR TO NIGEL FINCH, DON'T YOU? COULD YOU INVITE HIM ALONG TO MY BIRTHDAY PARTY NEXT FRIDAY?

WHY? DO YOU NEED SOMEONE TO MAKE UP THE NUMBERS?

NO . . . A FEW OF THE GIRLS HAVE BEEN ASKING IF HE'S GOING. YOUR BOY-NEXT-DOOR HAS GOT QUITE A FAN CLUB.

WHAT DO YOU MAKE OF THAT, LIZ? TWICE IN TWO DAYS! I MUST POP IN AND SEE NIGEL WHEN I GET HOME, TO TELL HIM HOW POPULAR HE IS.

HMM . . . IT'S ALL BEEN A BIT SUDDEN, THIS NEW-FOUND ATTENTION. MAYBE HE'S PUT AN ADVERT IN THE LOCAL PAPER, SAYING HE'S WON THE POOLS, OR SOMETHING.

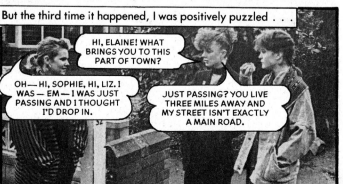

But the third time it happened, I was positively puzzled . . .

HI, ELAINE! WHAT BRINGS YOU TO THIS PART OF TOWN?

OH — HI, SOPHIE, HI, LIZ. I WAS — EM — I WAS JUST PASSING AND I THOUGHT I'D DROP IN.

JUST PASSING? YOU LIVE THREE MILES AWAY AND MY STREET ISN'T EXACTLY A MAIN ROAD.

WELL, TO TELL THE TRUTH, I WAS KIND OF HOPING NIGEL MIGHT BE AROUND. YOU HAVEN'T SEEN HIM RECENTLY, HAVE YOU?

NO, NOT FOR A COUPLE OF DAYS, AND QUITE HONESTLY, I'M BEGINNING TO WONDER IF NIGEL HAS UNDERGONE SOME MIRACULOUS CHANGE — HE'S MORE POPULAR IN THIS TOWN THAN PHILLIP SCHOFIELD AT THE MOMENT.

WELL, SOPHIE, HOW DOES IT FEEL TO BE LIVING NEXT DOOR TO THE LOCAL HEART-THROB?

INCREDIBLE. MAYBE I'M JUST BEING A BIT HARSH ON NIGEL, LIZ . . . I MEAN, I HAVE LIVED NEXT DOOR TO HIM FOR MOST OF MY LIFE, SO I'VE NEVER REALLY THOUGHT OF HIM AS A HUNK. WHAT DO YOU THINK?

YOU COULD BE RIGHT. BUT I THINK IT'S TIME YOU GAVE NIGEL AN EDUCATION, HE IS SIXTEEN, AFTER ALL — IT'S ABOUT TIME HE STARTED GOING OUT WITH GIRLS.

THAT'S HARDLY SURPRISING — NIGEL'S NICE-LOOKING AND HE'S A BETTER DANCER THAN PHILLIP SCHOFIELD! IF YOU SEE HIM, WILL YOU TRY AND GET HIM TO COME TO THE DISCO ON SUNDAY?

WELL, I'LL TRY, BUT I'M NOT MAKING ANY PROMISES. HE MIGHT BE IN A PHOTO SESSION OR SIGNING AUTOGRAPHS . . .

YES, IT IS. HE SPENDS FAR TOO MANY HOURS MUCKING ABOUT WITH THAT BIKE OF HIS. I THINK I'LL FIND AN EXCUSE TO GO AND SEE HIM TOMORROW . . .

So, the following day . . .

HIYA, NIGEL, HOW ARE YOU DOING?

OH, I'M FINE. THE BIKE HAS A SLOW PUNCTURE, THOUGH. I'M JUST WORKING ON IT OUT THE BACK.

OH, GOOD, I'LL COME AND HELP, WILL I? AFTER ALL, TWO HEADS ARE BETTER THAN ONE.

OH, RIGHT.

I MUST ADMIT, SOPHIE, I DIDN'T THINK YOU WERE INTERESTED IN BIKES.

ME, NOT INTERESTED? I LOVE BIKES! MY MUM SAYS I COULD RIDE BEFORE I COULD WALK.

WELL, YOU'VE CERTAINLY KEPT QUIET ABOUT IT IN THE PAST. COULD YOU PASS ME THAT SPANNER, SOPHIE?

OF COURSE, I DON'T DEVOTE MY WHOLE LIFE TO BIKES, UNLIKE YOU, NIGEL. I LIKE TO GET OUT A BIT, TOO — TO DISCOS AND THINGS.

HMM — THEY'RE NOT REALLY MY SCENE, I'M AFRAID. ALTHOUGH I DO LIKE TO PUT IN AN APPEARANCE AT THE CYCLISTS' BALL EVERY YEAR.

AND BY THE WAY THAT'S A HAMMER, SOPHIE, NOT A SPANNER!

I decided I'd wasted enough time on small talk . . .

LOOK, NIGEL, LET'S STOP BEATING ABOUT THE BUSH. NOW, I HAPPEN TO KNOW THAT SEVERAL OF THE MOST ELIGIBLE GIRLS IN TOWN HAVE BEEN EXPRESSING AN INTEREST IN YOU RECENTLY. PERSONALLY, I CAN'T SEE THE ATTRACTION, BUT I DO THINK IT'S TIME YOU WERE LAUNCHED INTO SOME SORT OF SOCIAL CIRCLE.

BUT, SOPHIE . . .

NO BUTS, NIGEL. WE'RE FRIENDS, AREN'T WE? WE'VE ALWAYS BEEN CLOSE, SO REALLY, I'M THE ONLY ONE WHO CAN TALK TO YOU LIKE THIS.

WELL, I DON'T KNOW . . .

AND IT'S BECAUSE WE'RE SUCH GOOD FRIENDS THAT I'VE DECIDED TO TAKE YOU UNDER MY WING. I'M GOING TO TURN YOU INTO SUCH A HUNK, YOUR OWN MOTHER WON'T RECOGNISE YOU.

WE'LL START TODAY. ONE OF THE MEN'S SHOPS IN TOWN HAS A SALE ON. I KNOW YOU'VE STILL GOT QUITE A BIT OF YOUR BIRTHDAY MONEY LEFT, SO WE'LL PUT IT TO GOOD USE.

NO, DON'T THANK ME. MY THANKS WILL BE THE EXPRESSIONS ON EVERYONE'S FACES AT KAREN'S PARTY NEXT WEEK. COME ON!

SOPHIE, I . . .

I could tell Nigel wasn't used to going shopping, but he seemed to enjoy himself . . .

RIGHT, WE'VE GOT THE TROUSERS. NOW WE'LL PICK OUT A NICE SHIRT. WHAT ABOUT BLUE?

BLUE'S NICE.

NO, ON THE OTHER HAND, THIS AQUAMARINE WOULD LOOK BETTER. WHAT DO YOU THINK?

LOVELY.

Next on the shopping list . . .

YOU REALLY NEED A GOOD, DISTINCTIVE AFTERSHAVE, NIGEL, SO THAT PEOPLE ASSOCIATE THAT SMELL WITH YOU. THIS ONE'S GREAT — SPICY, BUT WITH A HINT OF FRESH LEMON.

WHATEVER YOU THINK, SOPHIE.

EM . . . YOU DO SHAVE, DON'T YOU, NIGEL?

OH YES — AT LEAST ONCE A MONTH.

The finishing touch . . .

SO WHAT EXACTLY WOULD YOU LIKE, SIR? A SHORT CROP, PERHAPS, LEAVING A BIT OF LENGTH ON TOP?

THAT SOUNDS FINE.

NO! EM — I MEAN, NOTHING TOO DRASTIC . . .

Famous last words . . .

YOU LOOK GREAT, NIGEL — EXACTLY RIGHT. THE GIRLS ARE GOING TO LOVE YOU.

FROM WHAT YOU'VE BEEN TELLING ME, I THOUGHT THEY ALREADY DID.

OH, THEY DO, THEY DO. WITH THIS NEW LOOK, THOUGH, YOU'LL HAVE EVEN MORE ADMIRERS.

On the night of the party . . .

YOU LOOK BRILLIANT, NIGEL. NOW, A FEW WORDS OF ADVICE. PLAY IT COOL, SPREAD YOURSELF ABOUT A BIT. AND DON'T LET ELAINE BEATTIE GET HER CLAWS INTO YOU — SHE'LL NEVER LET YOU GO!

THANKS FOR THE WARNING. SHALL WE GO?

I think I felt more nervous than Nigel did by the time we arrived . . .

NIGEL! GREAT TO SEE YOU! COME ON, LET ME GET YOU A COKE. THERE ARE QUITE A FEW PEOPLE JUST DYING TO TALK TO YOU. HI, SOPHIE, HELP YOURSELF TO THE FOOD AND DRINK.

THANKS.

NOW I KNOW HOW THE INVISIBLE MAN FELT.

A couple of hours later . . .

SOPHIE, I'VE BEEN LOOKING FOR YOU! WHAT ARE YOU DOING IN HERE? YOU'RE USUALLY THE LIFE AND SOUL OF THE PARTY.

YEAH, WELL, I THINK NIGEL'S TAKEN OVER THAT JOB. I HAVEN'T SEEN HIM ALL NIGHT.

THAT SHOULD PLEASE YOU. YOU'RE USUALLY MOANING ABOUT HOW HE TRAILS AFTER YOU AND CLINGS TO YOU ALL THE TIME.

YEAH, I SUPPOSE YOU'RE RIGHT. LIZ, WHAT DO YOU THINK OF NIGEL? IS HE THE KIND OF BOY YOU COULD FANCY?

HMMM — MAYBE. I MEAN, I ALWAYS THOUGHT HE WAS CUTE. ANYWAY, HE WOULDN'T BE INTERESTED IN ME — HE ONLY HAS EYES FOR ONE GIRL.

WHO IS IT? IT'S SURELY NOT ELAINE!

USE SOME COMMON SENSE, SOPHIE. THE WHOLE THING WAS A SET-UP. IT'S YOU NIGEL FANCIES — HE HAS DONE FOR AGES, BUT HE KNEW YOU JUST THOUGHT OF HIM AS THE BOY-NEXT-DOOR.

HE GOT JILL AND ELAINE AND THE REST TO PRETEND THEY WERE KEEN ON HIM, JUST SO YOU'D LOOK AT HIM IN A DIFFERENT LIGHT. AND I THINK IT'S WORKED.

For once I was speechless . . .

SURELY NOT? ME . . . AND NIGEL FINCH FROM NEXT DOOR?

Just then . . .

SO YOU'RE IN HERE — I THOUGHT YOU'D DISAPPEARED. I'VE BEEN LOOKING FOR YOU.

OH . . . HAVE YOU?

THIS IS EMBARRASSING. I DON'T KNOW HOW TO ACT WITH HIM.

WHAT'S THAT?

YOU KNOW, SOPHIE, I HAVE TO THANK YOU FOR ALL THE TROUBLE YOU WENT TO OVER ME. THERE'S ONE THING YOU FORGOT TO TEACH ME ABOUT, THOUGH . . .

I'll say one thing for Nigel — he was a pretty fast learner . . .

THE END

Simon (Mmm Dreamy) Groom and Janet Ellis interview potential presenters in the Blue Peter garden in '84. That's Mark Curry second from the right.

Everyone who was anyone had legwarmers — fluorescent or lurex ones were best!

Some members of the Brat Pack pictured here on the set of the wonderful 'Breakfast Club'.

FASHION

Skirts were midi, A-line and hanging mid calf in the first few years but as the years progressed, so did skirts — upwards, and long, lean legs were a must! Skirt lengths and styles were not necessarily followed to a tee and anything from the flirtatious frilly puffball to the 50's-style 'swing' skirt was acceptable. Trousers underwent a dramatic change over the decade; from the snug-fitting jeans of the early 80's to the looser, more comfortable fit of chinos and lounge pants. The much hyped comeback of flares was promised but never fully materialised although trouser widths did increase substantially. As ever, denim played a great part in the fashion collections of the '80's, and despite the introduction of black denim (à la Eddie Kidd), blue denim reigned supreme, promoted by Nick Kamen and the infamous launderette!

Never before had so much attention been paid to details in the neckline, from grandpa shirts in '83 to polo necks in '86, and the off the shoulder, scooped and fichu necks of the final years.

The high, high and totally impractical heels of '80 and '81 came back to earth and for a good few years flat shoes and Doc Martens were the shoes to be seen in. However heels rose again with block, wedge and Louis heels of the late 80's.

DESIGNERS OF THE 80'S

Body Map	Jeff Banks
Jasper Conran	Valentino
John Galliano	Jean-Paul Gaultier

EVENTS

Live Aid was THE event of the '80's! One hot day in July '85 Wembley Stadium was filled to bursting with thousands of sweaty fans who turned out to support famine relief in Ethiopia and the Sudan, brought so forthrightly to public attention by ex-Boomtown Rats front-man, Bob Geldof, who was later knighted for his contribution not only to charity but more importantly in the long term to increasing public awareness of the terrible situations outside our country.

Other events include: The Miners' strike, 2 Royal weddings (81 and '86), The Falklands War, The AIDS terror, Hungerford massacre, Kings Cross Tube Disaster, Zeebruge Ferry Disaster, Earthquake in Mexico City, Football hooliganism at the Heisel Stadium in Belgium.

ENTERTAINMENT
Music: There were the 'come-backs', like Ben E. King, Marvin Gaye and the Bee Gees, there was rap, there was House, there were the

The 80's — Decade of jumbled fads, outrageous trends and nostalgia. Anything goes — that's the 80's!

THE 80's

More rather dodgy fashion items of the early 80's — pedalpushers, teamed with a rather lovely ruffled blouse and bolero. One, two, three — CRINGE!

Georgio Armani made a big name for himself in the 80's. Here it's back to school on the catwalk in '84 and later Jonathan Ross graced many an Armani suit in '87.

Granny Greene's kitchen curtains and toilet chain beautifully modelled by the fetching Sarah c. 1983.

wannabes (the one hit wonders who relied more on their looks than their talent to sell records — too numerous to mention!) and there was, believe it or not, some talent, namely Terence Trent D'Arby, Wham!, The Smiths, Scritti Politti, ABC, Lloyd Cole & the Commotions, BAD and selected others.

TV: Blue Peter was still going strong even though Jack and Jill died and Janet Ellis left — oh woe! Trendy telly was very much in evidence with Jonathan Ross's 'Last Resort', 'The Tube', 'The Chart Show', 'Network 7' and a series of magazine programmes. Comedy hit a lighter note with 'alternative comedy' — much funnier and a lot saucier with thanks to Ben Elton, Robbie Coltraine, Victoria Wood, Lenny Henry and Tracey Ullman!

Films: Horror films got scarier and scarier with new technology allowing spine chilling special effects, take 'House', 'Nightmare On Elm Street' and 'The Fly', for example! There were arty films like 'Betty Blue' and 'Diva' which didn't make a lot of sense but looked good anyway! And then there was the Brat Pack, a crowd of young American actors who took the world by storm with their talent and good looks. However, Britain was not far behind and produced the Brit Pack which included Rupert Everett, Jason Connery and other yummies!

FILMS OF THE 80'S

'Crocodile Dundee' 'Betty Blue'
'The Breakfast Club' 'Fatal Attraction'
'Ghostbusters' 'Angel Heart'

FADS

You name it and it's been a fad, most of them extremely cringeable but some of them are still going strong. Here's a selection of the best . . . and worst!

Vegetarianism Ripped 501's
Nose jobs Boxer shorts
Leggings Nostalgia
Leg warmers Plastic beach shoes
Braun Independents Personal stereos
Additive-free food CD's
Deely Boppers Fluorescents

Fashion à la 1982. Although Lesley's not so sure — that's just like the little number she's sporting today!

Those trendy foxtresses Mel & Kim hit the charts in a big way with boppy Eurobeat which they churned out with the help of producers extraordinaire — Stock, Aitken and Waterman.

Wham! THE teeny-bop sensation of the decade. What anyone finds sexy about a constipated ape, I don't know!

Paula Geldof (née Yates) — flirt of the decade, host of the 'Tube' and the media person most renowned for 'getting about a bit'! Her many relationships were surrounded by scandal and more than friendly links were rumoured with Ben Volpelière Pierrot, Terence Trent D'Arby, Duran Duran (what, all at once?) and Dr Robert from The Blow Monkeys, to name but a few!

Alternative, outrageous — the fashion of the 80's.

Increased awareness of our nosh. Nutrition information was provided on foods stating just how many E's you were shoving down you.

'EastEnders' — the soap of the 80's, topping 'Coronation Street' in the TV ratings with 22 million viewers weekly. Here, the cast are having a good ol' sing-song in the Queen Vic in '86. After 3 . . . My ol' man's a dustman . . .

The 80's wouldn't have been the 80's without Madonna. How many of you wore pearls round your wrists and dozens of crosses and chains round your neck just so you could look like her? Well I didn't for a start but I'm not a young poseur like you!

Candleglow Girl

The moment he saw her, so pale and lovely in the candlelight, he was under her spell. And he knew he didn't want to belong to Beth anymore . . .

56

H E would never forget the moment he saw her, in the candlelight, at Beth's party. She was tall and slim, pale and mysterious, with shining eyes and long, straight blonde hair melting into the flickering shadows.

She was standing just inside the doorway, looking lost. No one else seemed to have noticed her; they had all come alive with the sudden power cut. Someone had found batteries for the tape deck, others bustled around lighting candles, and he could hear Beth laughing in the kitchen.

"Are you looking for Beth?" he asked, coming towards her. "She's in the kitchen supervising the food."

"Thank goodness I'm at the right place," she told him with a little laugh. "The lights went out just as I walked in the door!"

The candlelight played on her face, and her smile was fascinating. He couldn't stop staring at her.

"I'm Gail," she told him, suddenly shy under his gaze.

"From Beth's class at college. You must be Ian."

"How do y'know?" he asked in surprise.

"Oh, Beth's talked a lot about you."

The candlelight flickered around them as he stood and stared. Suddenly, from the moment he'd set eyes on her, he didn't want to belong to Beth anymore.

"Gail! There you are! I was wondering where you'd got to!"

Beth came up behind him, slid her arm through his, and gave him a hug.

"I'm so lucky — so many lovely pressies!" she exclaimed as she took Gail's gift. "And candlelight, too! I think the best thing that happened this evening was the power cut."

She looked up at Ian. "Well, almost the best thing," she said softly as she touched the tiny gold locket round her neck. His gift to her. He knew she was remembering the moment he'd given it to her, the only time they had been alone that night. He remembered it too, but he felt guilty because that moment meant nothing to him now that he'd seen Gail.

"Oh Gail, it's beautiful, thank you!" cried Beth, as she unwrapped a long silk scarf. She took Gail's arm. "Now, come on, let's get down to real business. There's someone I want you to meet . . . See you later, Ian."

He didn't want Gail to go. He didn't want her to meet anyone else. He wanted her to stay near him, to talk to him. But it was impossible even to consider it at Beth's party.

He'd never dreamed that this would happen, that he could be with Beth but find himself totally wrapped up in thoughts of someone else. He just couldn't get Gail out of his mind and as the party went on he listened to her laughing and chatting with other people.

It was some time before he realised she was just as aware of him, too. Every time he looked her way, he caught her eyes slipping away, or her head turning a bit too quickly. But there was nothing he could do about it, at Beth's party.

"A RE you all right, Ian?" asked Beth, for the second time that night.

"Yeah, why?" He smiled as he looked down at her, aware that she'd been standing there for some time, and he was holding the same tape he'd picked up ten minutes ago. Beth. Small and dark. A nobody in the candlelight.

"You've been miles away all night."

"Oh, it's the candlelight. It's like being in a different world."

His smile was a lie. He had heard Gail laugh, and wanted to turn away, to find out who she was laughing with.

"It's wonderful," Beth said softly, squeezing his hand. "My party. My present. You."

He felt so guilty as he looked down at her. Things had changed, and would never ever be the same again. But he couldn't tell her that, at her party.

All the same, he knew he had to do something, he couldn't let Gail walk right out of his life.

"Let's eat," he suggested suddenly. "Stay here, Beth, and I'll fetch you something."

He went, without looking back, in a hurry because he wanted to get away from her quickly. He'd just seen Gail going alone into the kitchen.

S HE was standing staring at the candle on the table, an empty plate in her hand. When he came in, she turned to look at him.

"I thought . . ." he began nervously. ". . . I thought . . . I was wondering . . . I was wondering if you wanted to dance . . ."

"Do you really think that would be a good idea?" she asked softly. "At Beth's party?"

So she did feel the same. Her words proved it.

"You've been staring at me all evening," she murmured, facing him. "Don't you think Beth might notice?"

"Do you mind?" he asked helplessly. "One word and I'll go away . . . for good."

"Mind?" she asked in a low voice. "How could I mind? I just wish it had happened somewhere else, not here . . .at Beth's party."

He could dimly see her in the flickering glow of the candles, but he felt he knew her, this girl who'd walked into his life, never to be forgotten. He took a step towards her, then stopped. This was the point of no return. One more step and it would be too late.

But it was too late anyway. He held out his hands. He would never have believed it. Another girl, in his arms, at Beth's party.

He could remember whispering her name, and closing his eyes and kissing her. Then suddenly, she went rigid in his arms. And someone, somewhere, cried out.

T HE lights had come back on. The power cut was over, and they were standing in full bright light beside the open doorway of the kitchen. Everyone was looking at them — including Beth.

He didn't want to remember the way Beth stormed out of the room as Gail said quickly, "We'd better go."

He didn't want to

remember that long walk through the room full of angry, staring people. At last they closed the door behind them and in relief he turned to look at Gail.

He couldn't believe his eyes! Under the bright light of the hall lamp, she was a stranger.

She had thin bleached hair and too much eyeshadow. Her lipstick was smudged and the smooth outline of her face that had been so mysterious by candlelight was square and sharp. Even her eyes were hard and cold.

Something drained out of him as he stared at her. She smiled up at him uncertainly.

"I'd better get my coat," she said and her voice sounded harsh under the electric light. He nodded, at a loss for words. He watched her walk off along the hall, wobbling on her high heels, and the silver thread in her dress looked cheap and worn. What had happened to his candleglow girl?

As he stood there, he saw Beth standing in the shadows at the top of the stairs. Her eyes were dark and angry. Slowly she lifted her hands and pulled at the gold chain round her neck. She threw it at his feet and then she was gone.

He picked up the chain slowly, feeling guilty, stupid and sad.

He heard the door close softly and he turned round, hopefully, but the glittery eyes and the red lipped smile were the same. A stranger's. Gail came towards him smiling, but his candleglow girl had gone forever.

57

THE BIG BINGE!

Food is, as any of the BJ gang will tell you, berrilliant. We can't live without it, dontcha know? But we *can* live without supplementing our daily intake with sneaky (or not so sneaky) McDonalds, or without a coupla choccie bars for pudding. It's difficult to curb a chocolate craving or a junk food fad, but take our word for it, if the man of the moment takes you out for el posho meal, and you've wolfed down half your pizza while he's still on his olive, he won't be greatly impressed. And it's a sad fact, too, that your bathroom scales won't thank you for it, nosiree! Try, if you can, to substitute that stodge for some crisps or fruit. Be kind to your bod!

NAIL BITING!

Bleee! There's nothing more of a turn-off than reaching for someone's hand only to be met with the sight of ragged and stubby nails. Inch-long talons may not be everyone's cup of tea either, admittedly, but if you think about it, all that chomping ain't going to do your teeth much good. And what's more, the sight of you constantly gnawing at your finger doesn't exactly give that certain sophisticated image we all strive for, eh, style snoots?

SMOKING!

Ask any hardened smoker, and we bet our bottom Wispa that they'll advise you in the strongest possible terms not to start smoking. It's expensive, it's ugly, and more than anything it gunges up your system like nothing else does. And it goes without saying (though we'll say it anyway) that the worst reason to start smoking in the first place is because "everyone else does it". Show your individuality and in the long run you'll be

Admit it, the last time you pigged out on chocolate probably wasn't too long ago! Or you might be partial to a touch of nail-gnawing now and then. Or maybe you're a nicotine addict — yeugh! Whatever your weakness, chances are it ain't doing you a whole lot of good.

So what're you going to do about your bad habit then, eh? Learn to kick it, that's what! Here's our top ten of Big Bad Habits — see if yours is amongst 'em . . .

KICK IT!

more respected for it. If you feel odd without a cigarette then try chewing low-sugar gum or nibbling on a carrot. After all, what's best — looking "the part" now, or five minutes off your life with every cigarette you smoke? The choice is yours!

PICKING YOUR ZITS/SCABS/ TOENAILS/NOSE!

Nuff said!

NOT CHANGING YOUR UNDIES EVERY DAY!

"What if you get run over by a bus and end up in hospital?" as our mums said to us . . .

SNIFFING — CONSTANTLY!

This, and wiping your nose on your sleeve, must be one of the most truly repulsive things known to mankind and BJ.

And it's a really easy habit to start, too. But just wait until you're sitting on the bus and the bloke beside you starts snorting and continues it all the journey: you'll see for yourself how offensive it is!

SHOPLIFTING!

Well! Now here's an extremely habit-forming occupation. It may be "just teensy" things "they won't miss", but shoplifting just isn't on and really isn't worth the cheap thrills, honest injun. So next time any so-called mates are planning a "shopping spree" and tell you it'll be a good laugh, just tell them that the thought of going to court doesn't seem a hoot to you, OK?

GAMBLING!

Slot machines and lottery tickets can turn into prettee nastee addictions. The thrill of winning keeps you coming

back for more and soon there's no stopping you. But as any statistic snoot'll find pleasure in telling you, the actual chances of your winning are roughly a squillion to one. Which basically means you have to part with a lorra loot to get any return. Pretty pointless, really . . .

BOOZING!

Drinking alcohol, particularly if you're underage, is *reallllly* immature and can be dangerous 'cos it's so easy to lose control. Need we say more?

FIBBING!

Another very easy habit to form. One of the main reasons that the occasional white lie grows into something more is that some folk think it makes them more interesting if they pretend that Rick Astley's going out with them or that they used to live in the Bahamas. However, one of the main reasons that fibbing isn't such a clever idea is that more often than not, it backfires and everybody finds out that the closest you came to the Bahamas was going on the bus past Heathrow Airport and that "Rick Astley" is in fact Specky from round the corner. Specky'd be none too chuffed, neither!

Other undesirable habits which the BJ Gang have a particular hatred for include slurping your tea, cleaning your ears in public, speaking with your mouth full, talking loudly at the cinema (this is a *really* bad one!), spitting (there's no excuse for that at all) and constantly interrupting.

If you can *honestly* say you don't do any of these things, then we'd like to hear from you — what's your secret?? And if we've caught you out, then all you have to do is — KICK IT!

There was one thing that brightened up my boring job at the café . . .

THEY'RE IN HERE EVERY LUNCH-TIME, HEATHER, JUST CHATTING AND LAUGHING. THEY LOOK SO HAPPY. DOESN'T IT MAKE YOU JEALOUS?

COUNTER ATTRACTION

OH, IT'S YOUR ROMANTIC COUPLE AGAIN, IS IT? STILL, I SUPPOSE THEY'RE MORE INTERESTING TO WATCH THAN THE USUAL GOINGS ON IN HERE.

WELL, IF THEY CAN BE HAPPY TOGETHER EVEN IN A TACKY PLACE LIKE THIS, THEN TRUE LOVE MUST EXIST.

TELL YOU WHAT, LOUISE, GET YOURSELF A BOYFRIEND THEN TELL ME IF YOU STILL THINK THE SAME.

CHANCE WOULD BE A FINE THING!

THIS IS THE CLOSEST I EVER GET TO A ROMANTIC ENCOUNTER — WATCHING OTHER PEOPLE!

Just then . . .

EXCUSE ME, YOUNG LADY, BUT THIS SCONE IS TOTALLY STALE! I —

COULD I JUST LEAVE THIS MONEY WITH YOU? I'M IN A BIT OF A HURRY.

SURE.

WELL! HOW RUDE! I HAPPEN TO BE FIRST IN THE QUEUE, YOUNG MAN!

SORRY. IT'S HARDLY SENSIBLE TO YELL AT THE STAFF, THOUGH, IS IT? YOU'D BE BETTER OFF ASKING TO SEE THE MANAGER.

EM, I'LL JUST CHANGE IT, SHALL I?

Many apologies later . . .

SO, WHAT'S A NICE GIRL LIKE YOU DOING IN A PLACE LIKE THIS?

SOMETIMES I WONDER — BUT A JOB'S A JOB, AT THE MOMENT.

WELL, IT SEEMS TO ME YOU'RE WORTH SOMETHING BETTER. STILL, KEEP SMILING.

HE'S SO NICE. HIS GIRLFRIEND'S VERY LUCKY . . . I JUST HOPE MR PEARCE DOESN'T GET TO HEAR ABOUT WHAT HAPPENED TODAY.

However . . .

AND IN FUTURE, IF A CUSTOMER HAS A COMPLAINT, YOU DEAL WITH IT PROMPTLY. THE LADY SAID YOU LOOKED STRAIGHT PAST HER.

SORRY, MR PEARCE. IT WON'T HAPPEN AGAIN.

RIGHT. THEN LET'S HAVE NO MORE DAY-DREAMING, OR YOU MIGHT FIND YOURSELF AT THE JOB CENTRE.

I'M BEGINNING TO THINK THAT MIGHT BE THE BEST THING ALL ROUND.

BUT THEN I WOULDN'T BE ABLE TO FOLLOW THE PROGRESS OF THAT COUPLE. I'LL BET HE'LL GET DOWN ON ONE KNEE AND PROPOSE ANY DAY NOW.

And next day . . .

THERE HE IS, THE ROMANTIC HERO . . . BUT WHERE'S HIS GIRLFRIEND?

HI! WHAT WOULD YOU LIKE TODAY?

JUST A COFFEE, PLEASE.

OH, HE LOOKS REALLY FED UP. SOMETHING MUST HAVE GONE WRONG.

EM . . . JUST THE ONE CUP?

YEAH, I'M ON MY OWN TODAY. WE HAD A BIG ROW ABOUT MY QUEUE-JUMPING YESTERDAY, AMONGST OTHER THINGS.

And . . .

SOMEHOW I FEEL RELIEVED. IT'S ABOUT TIME I STARTED TO PUSH FOR WHAT I REALLY WANT INSTEAD OF JUST PUTTING UP WITH WHATEVER'S AVAILABLE. I'M GLAD I'LL NEVER HAVE TO FACE THAT GROTTY PLACE AGAIN.

IF IT'S ANY CONSOLATION I'LL NEVER DRINK HIS COFFEE AGAIN.

ME NEITHER. IT WAS AWFUL, ANYWAY. SORRY FOR CAUSING YOU SO MUCH TROUBLE.

IT'S OK. I HATED THE JOB, ACTUALLY. I'M GLAD TO SEE YOU TWO BACK TOGETHER, THOUGH.

OH, WE'RE OK — WE'RE ALWAYS ARGUING BUT WE ALWAYS MANAGE TO MAKE UP.

MMM, WELL, I'D BETTER GET OFF TO MEET LIONEL. I'M LATE AS IT IS!

EH?

SISTERS! WHO'D HAVE THEM? STILL, AT LEAST SHE KNOWS HOW TO MAKE A TIMELY EXIT.

S-SISTER? SHE'S YOUR SISTER? I THOUGHT SHE WAS YOUR GIRLFRIEND!

OH, NO! HEAVEN FORBID! SHE'D NEVER STOP NAGGING . . . IT'S YOU I'VE HAD MY EYE ON FOR AGES.

ME?

ANY MOMENT NOW I'M GOING TO WAKE UP.

YEAH, YOU. SO HOW ABOUT GOING FOR A COFFEE — IN SOME OTHER CAFE, OF COURSE?

WHY NOT?

LET SOMEBODY ELSE DO THAT WATCHING FOR A CHANGE.

THE END

The "Oh No, I Know This One, What Is It Again?" Really Annoying Pop Quiz...

So you think you're a girlie-swot when it comes to pop? Try answering our tricky questions about Madonna, Rick Astley and Wet Wet Wet and see if you're right . . .

ARE YOU A WETS WHIZZ-KID?

1. Where does the name Wet Wet Wet come from?
2. What was Marti's rather unusual job before he became el megastar?
3. Who insists he's never been in lurve?
4. Who's the midget in the band?
5. Who used to have green hair?
6. Who would the band like to play a support slot with?
7. What did the lads' insist should be written into their contract before signing to Phonogram Records?
8. What's their fave food?
9. Who's described as being the most serious member of the band?
10. Which film series would they like to write a theme song for?

DO YOU RAVE ABOUT RICK?

1. When was the lad born? (Exact date, puh-lease!)
2. What does Rick say he's addicted to?
3. He's a clean-cut boy now. But what sort of music was he into as a teenager?
4. Where does he occasionally work when he has some spare time?
5. What was his first task for Stock, Aitken and Waterman?
6. What band did he sing with before becoming el big solo star?
7. What irritates Rick more than anything else in the whole wide world and Africa?
8. Is he a romantic lad or a birrova raver?
9. What was his first single?
10. What's Rick's full name?

MAD ABOUT MADDY?

1. Who does Madonna idolise, music-wise?
2. Who starred alongside Madonna in "Who's That Girl"?
3. When was her first Top 40 hit and what was the song?
4. What height is she?
5. Who does Madonna want to be as famous as?
6. What was her earliest ambition?
7. What scares Madonna?
8. What is Madonna's view of nuns?
9. Who was her "True Blue" album dedicated to?
10. Which band did Madonna lurve as a nipper?

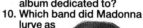

Terence
Trent D'arby

Sole

POINTY SHOES

Pointy shoes, the chiropodist's nightmare and a Gothic's fashion essential, are worn by people who like black. Goths are pretty morbid people: with pale, pale faces, black, black eye make-up and red, red lipstick. Clothes are black, with maybe a dash of purple for special occasions, but generally it's a black tassle skirt, black shirt, black coat and black shoes, even in the heat of the summer it's black, black, black. These pointy winkle-pickers come in a variety of styles in suede and leather with any number of buckles. The Goth will wear these to the local dark 'n' sweaty discos where she listens to music like The Sisters of Mercy, This Mortal Coil, The Swans and other such swirly solemn bands. Hobbies are 'strange' to say the least and include watching spooky films like 'Eraserhead' and anything about Dracula, Vampires or Transylvania; meeting with the dead in dark graveyards, sleeping in coffins and collecting crucifixes and anything black also rate high on the gothic fun 'n' cheery pastimes list!

66

WHERE WOULD WE BE WITHOUT A GOOD PAIR OF SHOES? (IN THE CHIROPODIST'S SURGERY, OF COURSE! — SMARTY-PANTS ED.) OUR CHOICE OF SHOES SAYS A LOT ABOUT THE TYPE OF PERSON WE ARE; ARE YOU A SNAPPY STILETTO SPORTER OR A DOC MARTEN DUDE? READ ON TO FIND OUT!

12" DOCTOR MARTEN BOOTS

12" DM's, commonly worn by skinheads, heavies and the like, are hardly the most dainty or feminine of booties, but they score high for practicality. Girls who wear these are usually tough 'n' mean but that doesn't go to say that they're bad company! Dressed in her Docs, ripped jeans, a biker's jacket all held together with safety pins she may look pretty formidable but underneath it all she's likely to be insecure and as quiet as a lamb.

She likes heavy rocking music like Saxon, Def Leppard, Whitesnake, Black Sabbath and a multitude of other sounds guaranteed to explode Granny's hearing aid! Hobbies include motorbikes, going to sweaty dark stomping gigs, head banging and getting forehead tattoos!

For added impact and scary factor, such girls tend to hang around in mobs with equally tough guys with freaky haircuts and scars down their cheeks.

Mates!

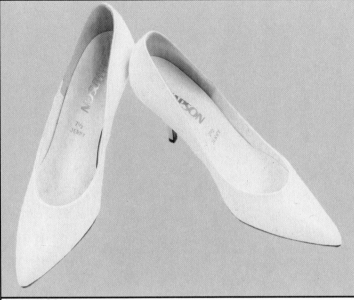

STILETTOS

Let me introduce you to Stacey-Marie. She really is a character, often to be found at the local disco with her equally charming pals, dancing round their stylish handbags to the funky (?) sounds of Samantha Fox's latest 'hits'! You won't see her anywhere without those beloved stilettos, except at the disco of course where she kicks them off to dance to her heart's content, barefoot. She owns stilettos in a range of colours from red to fluorescent yellow, but her real faves are her white ones with the 3 inch heel which she likes to wear with her tight white mini complete with 6 inch split up the back and her Benetton T-shirt. In fact she likes her white stilettos so much that she's got delightful white streaks put in her hair to match them! The shoes were a real bargain, too! Only 25p from "What Every Woman Wants". She's had them for a good 4 days now and the PVC at the bottom of the heel's only just starting to fray! All in all, a real style queen is our Stacey!

DOCTOR MARTEN SHOES

These days the Doctor Marten and the trendee go hand in hand. Usually worn with over-the-knee socks or hoop tights they are not only fashionable but highly practical into the bargain. DM's are available in shiny or waxed, wine or black or even with natty yellow stitching around the wondrous oil, fat, acid, petrol and alkali resistant sole. Although basically quite plain, the DM can be jazzed up in a variety of ways to suit your every taste and outfit; tartan ribbon as laces for that fetching Black Watch number, safety pins for the funky punky look, or just plain black laces for a more sophisticated look — well, as sophisticated as one can be in a bum-freezing mini, gingham braces and white polo!

But watch out, for trendees are a fast growing group of girlies who watch the fashion pages like hawks and talk about clothes, new bands, and other such trendy issues.

TRAINERS

Trainers are, as a rule, the mark of a casual. The casual is usually found hanging about in large mobs at football stadiums and on street corners. What they do there is something of a mystery but they do attend these corners with monotonous regularity and apparently pass the time of day chewing gum and sussing out the talent.

Although the trainer is generally regarded as 'sportswear' the only exercise these lot get is walking to and from football matches.

Casuals 'co-ordinate' their trainers with an assortment of outfits, usually checked jeans, or possibly a tight navy polyester skirt worn with bare legs and ankle socks, usually of the fluorescent variety!

To top these fetching get-ups you can bet your Chelsea Girl budget account that there'll be a Nike cagoul or adidas sweatshirt. Trainers are practical and durable and usually come in white, grey or black; particular favourites are Reeboks, Nikes, or the trustee adidas Samba.

DOLLY PUMPS

These little cutees are definitely for the innocents amongst us, that's why I'm wearing them myself! (Oh aye! — The Ed.) They're for the darling little Mummy's girls who never swear, never bitch, never stay up after 9 p.m. and drink a pint of milk every day! The ones who spend every spare moment, that's when they're not at Bible class, Guides, or staying late at school to help the teachers, doing their knitting, baking, reading or perfecting the latest techniques with a crochet hook!

Other hobbies include brisk daily walks in the park cosily wrapped up in Marks & Spencers latest 'fashions' i.e. brown woolly coat buttoned up to the chin, orange scarf, wool bobble hat and panda ear muffs.

Probably the most sensible footwear ever, with no chance of corns, bunions, blisters or any other nasties!

SO YOU'VE HAD ENOUGH OF ROB LOWE
AND TOM CRUISE? WELL CHECK OUT THE
SHAPE OF BRAT PACKERS TO COME, THE
YOUNG ONES WHO ARE MAKING THEIR
MARK ON THE AMERICAN MOVIE SCENE.
YES, THERE SEEMS TO BE A NEVER
ENDING SUPPLY OF HUNKY NEW TALENT
TO SWOON OVER! ALL WE CAN SAY IS
"KEEP 'EM COMING!"

BABY BRATS

KIRK CAMERON

JASON BATEMAN

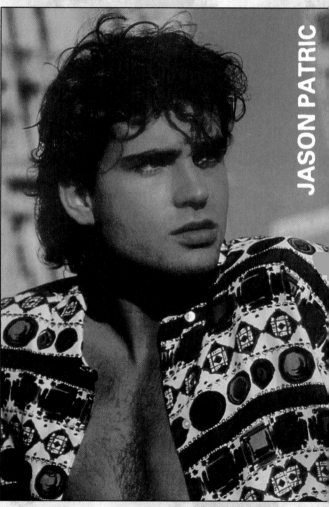

JASON PATRIC

68

Swoon, faint! This mystery man goes by the name of Kirk Cameron. He's an enormous star in America (no, he's quite normal sized actually, ha! — The Ed), and you should be able to see him in the film 'Like Father Like Son' any time now. In it, Kirk plays Chris Hammond, who switches brains with his dad! (What a spooky concept, eh readers?) His dad is actually played by the v. famous English actor Dudley Moore, but Kirk says that he didn't feel at all nervous about working with him. "Dudley worked hard at making me feel comfortable when we were filming," he says. "After only two days on the set we all felt really good and had a good laugh." Kirk's "date" in the film is played by Cami Cooper who has no end of praise for him. "He's a super guy. He's really dedicated to his work, and is incredibly talented. As a person he's just plain wonderful!" We couldn't agree more, Cami!

Jason Bateman first graced our Great British TV sets as David Hogan in the TV show 'Valerie', but shot to real mega stardom in 'Teen Wolf Too'. This boy has real Brat Pack connections, as his sister Justine stars alongside Michael J. Fox in 'Family Ties'.

He was born on January 14th, 1969 in Westchester, New York and is 5' 11" tall. He says he'd eventually like to go to college some day (what a waste!). Ha! But he also says that if leaving the "business" for four years is going to hurt his career, then he might think about putting it off for a while. (Phew!) Jason doesn't exactly have a "rawk 'n' roll" lifestyle, though, even with all his fame and fortune. When not filming he says he spends his time "at the movies or on the beach or we get a whole bunch of people together and play football." He also loves driving and spends a lot of time cruising around town in his Scirocco Turbo. Woo! Perhaps not one of the most exciting movie men we know, but we like him just the way he is!

Jason's full name is the same as his famous dad's — Jason Patric Miller (who played the priest in that spooky classic 'The Exorcist'). His mum is also an actress and brother Joshua appears in the film 'The River's Edge'. What talent! Jason didn't want to keep his family name however, and would rather be successful without having to rely on his relations' reputations.

Jason's film credits include 'Solarbabies' and 'The Lost Boys', and rumour has it that he's been romantically linked with Jami Gertz. He's worked with her on various TV programmes and plays, but claims his fellow 'Lost Boy' is "just a good friend". Well! He shuns the idea that he's a sex symbol. "That is something I definitely *don't* want," he says. Well, we're *sorry* Jason, but you definitely are one, so there!

COREY HAIM

Corey Haim was born in Toronto, Canada on December 23, 1971, but moved with his family to Los Angeles so that he could pursue his acting career. It certainly seems to have paid off, since Corey has so far acted in 'Platoon', 'Murphy's Romance', 'Lucas' and that shiversome chiller 'The Lost Boys'. He says he really enjoyed making that movie. "I made a lot of new friends, had lots of fun and hopefully made a movie that a lot of people are going to enjoy." Well, we did enjoy it, didn't we?! Corey loves racquetball (quaint American sport), *all* girls and sushi — which, fact fans, happens to be Japanese raw fish (bloog!). He's 5' 6" tall and had blue eyes and sandy brown hair and says he's "looking for a girl with a good personality. I'd hate it if a girl was only going out with me 'cos I'm in the movies." Well, as far as we're concerned, Corey's a megahunk, famous or otherwise!

RALPH MACCHIO

You'll probably know Ralph Macchio best for his part in the movies 'Karate Kid I' and 'II'. And you'll probably also know that Ralphy babes is one of the most fanciable young stars of the Brat Pack today. Unfortunately for us, though, it's "hands off" as a couple of years ago he was married to Phyllis Fierro. Bet you didn't know *that!* Worra waste! Ralph is actually rather a shy boy, and isn't very keen on all the media attention that's been bestowed upon him. He says he "doesn't feel comfortable talking about himself" and likes to keep family and friends as the most important parts of his life.

Ralph got his first big break in 'The Outsiders', a v. deep Francis Ford Copolla movie that also featured Rob Lowe, Tom Cruise and Matt Dillon, and was remembered by the others as being very serious about his acting. He preferred to spend his time studying lines and analysing the character he played to socialising on location. Imagine having the chance to party on down with that lot and having an early night instead! Ralph also dedicates a lot of time to visiting homeless kids in America. By jiggins, he's too good to be true!

69

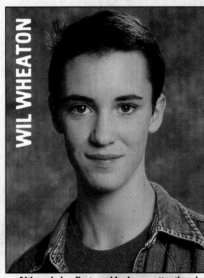

WIL WHEATON

Although he first grabbed our attention in 'Stand By Me', Wil Wheaton wasn't loafing around before, no sirree! He began making commercials at the tender age of seven and took part in loads of American TV specials.

When he's not working he loves to go to the beach, which is quite easy for him as he lives in California. "I love listening to the waves and watching the ocean," he sighs. (We have to ask ourselves if this guy is a closet hippy!) He was born on July 29th, 1972 and is 5' 7" tall. Sounds good? Well, Wil readily admits that he's available and says he loves "girls with great eyes". Don't all rush at once!

A GOOD FRIEND . . .

- will tell you if you have bad breath or BO. But gently does it!
- will keep a secret if you ask her to.
- will be completely honest with you and expect the same back.
- would probably borrow some money from you, but would ensure you got it back promptly.
- doesn't mind if you can't afford to buy her a birthday present.
- never forgets your birthday!
- always has a free shoulder to cry on.
- never forces you to break your diet, and doesn't scoff Big Macs in front of you when you're on one!
- doesn't just like you for your funky, football-playing, trendy, big bruv.
- knows your favourite kind of chocolate, and has a bar ready for when you're depressed.

A NOT-VERY-GOOD FRIEND . . .

- gets off with your boyfriend behind your back.
- tells all your intimate secrets to all and sundry.
- borrows your best blouse and returns it with a scorch mark — but claims to know nothing about it.
- says "You look great!" when you model your newly acquired skin-tight-dress-made-for-beanpoles, when in fact maternity dresses would be more your style.
- yells "Oi, Trace, there's that bloke you'd like to get yer hands on!" when Mr Funksome himself saunters by (leaving both you and he wishing the ground would open up and swallow the pair of you).
- arranges a foursome and leaves you with the ugly one.
- reminds you of every time she beat you in exams: and remembers the marks, too.
- spends hours discussing all your faults with your mother — in front of you!
- owes you at least a tenner but always seems to have enough to buy yet another article of clothing.
- wins a once-in-a-lifetime trip for two to New York to meet Curiosity . . . and doesn't take you!

FRIEND C

So what is it that sparks off a lifelong friendship? And who makes friends with you? And what's so good about friends anyway? We tried to find out.

Gail, Tara and Jenny are all 19 and met at college where they are doing Business Studies. What started off their friendship? Gail explained, "Well, two years ago when we started college we were staying in halls of residences. We discovered that we had a common bond of hatred — we hated the food and we hated the

people. In fact, the only things we didn't hate were ourselves!"

"Now Gail and I share a flat," Tara carried on, "and although we sometimes go around in a crowd, generally it's just the three of us. We have a great laugh together and it's not bitchy (well not about each other!) or imbalanced."

"That's true," said Jenny. "I do have some close friends outwith college but I don't feel the need for more close freinds at college than Tara and Gail. Where do we go when we go out? Oh, just to the Students' Union and to cafés. Monday night is pictures night, but — well, I've got a heavy date this week so . . . cut!"

Paul is 22 and met Leigh, 18, when he moved into Leigh's flat three months ago. They discovered that they had a common bond of loving Indie music like the Jesus and Mary

Chain, and they shared the same wacky sense of humour. Leigh was also swayed by the fact that Paul was very generous with his money! "We have a great laugh together," said Paul, "and I'm quite new in town so Leigh shows me good places to go like various studenty places." "We probably confide in each other a bit but our friendship's more based on having a good time rather than getting all deep and involved with each other's lives. We've got a mixed crowd of people we both see but no girlfriends at the moment." (Any offers, girls?)

"Can I say hello to my mum?" asks Paul. "Hi, Mum!"

Stuart and Pamela are both cooks and met at work a couple of years ago. It's unusual for two people of opposite sexes to be close friends without any romantic involvement, so we asked them about that: "That's true, I suppose," agreed Pamela. "Actually, we did go out with each other in the beginning but now we just enjoy each other's company. He's my best friend and he's such a good laugh. I don't feel odd 'cos he's a guy rather than a girl — and I do have some close girlfriends, too." "We tell each other everything and share a common hatred of other people at work!" laughs Stuart. "Sometimes I get teased, but it's all in jest. Pamela is a great friend and I couldn't wish for more."

Jenny, Susan and Katie are all 14 and are in the same year at school. They've been friendly for three years. "We're about as friendly as we could be considering we all live a good

R FOE?

Friends — where would we be without 'em? Well, we'd probably be a bit lonely, that's for sure. But what's so good about having them?

distance away from each other and transport is very difficult," explains Susan. "That's about right," Katie continues. "We see each other in school though and have good bitching sessions. I'm actually more friendly with a couple of girls who I'd say were my *best* friends, but Jenny, Susan and I have great laughs together."

"Probably Susan and I are best friends," says Jenny. "We confide in each other a lot. In fact, I think she knows all my deepest, darkest secrets."

TWO GIRLS TELL US THEIR OPINIONS OF FRIENDSHIP . . .

LINDSEY is 17 and has been friends with Alison since they were both nine. "We were in the same classes at school together. Actually I hated Alison at first. And I don't really remember when I decided I liked her, but we've been virtually inseparable since then anyway. There's nothing I couldn't tell Alison, though sometimes I know she might not approve. She'd always tell me, too, if she didn't like what I was doing. We know each other so well, actually, that we rarely argue 'cos we can sense each other's moods really easily. And I trust her implicitly. But others must think we're a bit odd 'cos we have a common sense of humour and can be rolling about for ages at really insignificant things that no one else would understand! No, I don't really need more 'best friends' than just Alison — she's the best!"

JACQUIE is also 17. "I wouldn't say I have a 'best friend', really. There are six or seven folk I'd regularly see, both boys and other girls, and we all get on with each other on more or less equal terms. If I had to single out anyone as a best friend it'd probably be Dave, another in my 'crowd'. It's easier to confide in a guy as you don't get the bitchiness associated with girls — and Dave's got the male insight, hasn't he? It's not without its problems, though — some boyfriends don't really understand our friendship. Sure, the gang has its arguments, but they're usually patched up pretty quickly — otherwise there's a lot of backstabbing and nobody's any happier that way. Sometimes I do miss having a really close friend, but at least this way I'm never short of someone to go out with. Really, I'm not really the kind of person who can get *that* close to one person. I think eventually, I would begin to get annoyed by them and find the friendship too stifling."

**Nicola Gaunt
Age 15**
Nicola has very fair skin and doesn't usually wear make-up. She wanted to look "different" but not too overdone! She didn't want her hair to be styled into a look that she couldn't achieve herself. The BJ team put their heads together and set to work . . .

**Dylan Drummond
Age 17**
Dylan, like his girlfriend Nicola, is lucky enough not to be troubled with spots, so he was off to a head start in the looks stakes! He admitted that his hair tended to be "totally unmanageable" and that a touch of gel or mousse just wasn't enough to control it! He wanted us to give him a little style clothes-wise, and didn't want to look "too normal or boring!" Well, we didn't want that either, did we?!

72

**Helen Rattray
Age 15**
Helen has fair skin, and apart from the odd blemish or two doesn't often have any bother with spots. She doesn't usually wear much make-up, but wanted her face "brightened up a bit" because it was quite pale. Although her hair does have a little bit of a perm in it, she said it still tended to be dead straight and didn't seem to stay in any sort of style. We'd soon sort that out though!

**Mark Smith
Age 16**
Mark told us he didn't really mind what we did to him as long as we covered up his spots and didn't make his hair "all freaky!" As far as clothes were concerned, Mark wanted to look "fairly normal" but smart. He said he didn't like clothes which were uncomfortable to wear. So we soon set about finding him a smarter look!

Don't you often wish you could be given a stylish new look? Two of our readers came along with their boyfriends to help us prove that making up isn't hard to do!

NEW

FACES!

MAKE-UP AND HAIR

While everyone sat waiting (just a little nervously!) in our photographer's studio, make-up artist Susie Kennett set to work on Nicola. She started by smothering Nicola's hair in masses of gel.

Because Nicola hadn't wanted a complicated style, all Susie did was to comb the gel through the hair, smoothing it back off the face.

To achieve a little quiff and kiss-curl, she simply picked out a small section of hair at the front, flicked it with the comb, and shaped the curl carefully with her fingers. Susie then applied a very light foundation which suited Nicola's fair complexion. It was set with translucent face powder before work started on the eyes!

Rusty red shades of eyeshadow were applied to the upper eyelids, blended right up to the brows, and the eyes were outlined with a touch of brown shadow and pencil. Colour was shaded into the eye socket line using a medium-sized make-up brush. Black eyeshadow was used to give definition to the eyebrows and was applied with a brow brush.

The final touches of colour were just a little rust-coloured blusher and a very natural pink lipstick.

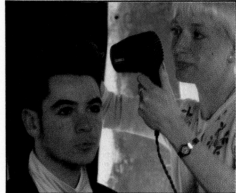

Dylan gets the brush off from Susie!

It was Dylan's turn next, and Susie started by spraying his hair with firm hold hairspray and blow-drying it back into a quiff. It was given another good blast of spray just to make sure there wasn't a hair out of place!

His face was given a light covering of translucent foundation for an even tone.

Susie used a little concealer under Dylan's eyes to hide the slight shadows.

As he has fairly heavy eyebrows, they were shaped into place using a brow brush.

Helen's new look began to take shape with Susie using heated rollers by Clairol on her hair. This would help to pep up her perm, without drying out the hair too much.

While the hair was setting, Susie applied a light foundation to Helen's face and set it with loose translucent face powder.

73

As Helen doesn't normally wear much make-up, Susie kept the eyes looking natural using beige shadows along the browline and light browns on the lids, blending up to the socket line.

To accentuate her eyebrows, black eyeshadow was applied to them using a brow brush. The eyes were then outlined with a soft brown pencil and smudged so there were no harsh lines.

Two coats of mascara were applied and just a touch of natural blusher to add more colour to her face. Helen's lips were then outlined with a red lip pencil and filled in with a bright red lipstick applied with a fine lip brush.

The heated rollers were removed from her hair, and Susie simply ran her fingers lightly through the curls just to loosen them slightly. This gave Helen's hair much more body.

To show off more of her newly made-up face, a top section of Helen's hair was twisted into a little knot and secured with a hairpin and plenty of hairspray.

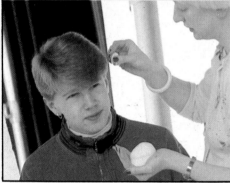

Mark looks a bit concerned about what's going on his hair!

Susie applied a light foundation to Mark's face, along with concealer to cover the few spots he had.

As he didn't want to look "freaky", all we did to his hair was to flatten the sides slightly with mousse. The fringe was given more of a layered look with mousse, and the hair was swept back slightly more from the face.

CLOTHES

Nicola and Helen are both very slim so they could have worn anything and still looked good! For Nicola though, we decided to go for a black top and skating skirt finished off with a tartan cummerbund. The outfit was then matched with long stripey socks which looked great!

Dylan was given a black suit with cropped jacket and an embroidered high-collared shirt.

For Helen, we chose a short beige jacket and taupe-coloured skating skirt. To brighten up the outfit, we added a colourful T-shirt.

A brown corset belt and cream over-the-knee socks completed the look.

Mark wore a taupe-coloured shirt with a brightly-patterned tie and dark-olive coloured cord trousers. Instead of a jacket, he was given a checked hooded jersey.

Nicola — "I'm really pleased with the look — I feel really trendy! The make-up looks great without being caked on and I could style my own hair easily this way if I was going somewhere special. I liked the clothes, too — they go with the hair and make-up. Dylan looks different, but really nice in his suit!"

Dylan — "I didn't think anyone could get my hair to stay off my face like that! My skin looks better with this foundation on. As far as the clothes go, I thought these were really stylish and not boring at all! They matched well with Nicola's outfit, too. Her hair and make-up look brilliant!"

75

Helen — "I'm going to wear red lipstick from now on! The make-up was very natural-looking and the lipstick really did brighten my face up. I usually wear my hair down, but the little knot on the top made it a bit more interesting and I loved all those fluffy curls! Mark's hair looks much tidier and he really suits a tie!"

Mark — "The tie is a bit like something out of Jonathan Ross's wardrobe, but it does jazz up the outfit a bit. My hair's nicer — the fringe doesn't look too floppy now. I feel quite smart and the clothes are comfortable. Helen looks great in those clothes and her hair and face are nice, too!"

Blind Date

BILLIAM IDOL AND MADONNA

Although they're both romantically entangled with others, Billy and Madonna would be sure to have a great time of it were they to spend an evening together. Both say their image is really tongue-in-cheek and basically for a laugh and they'd be bound to get along. They're also both vain so they could both have a great time giving each other wacky fashion and beauty tips, discussing the best brand of hairspray to use etc. (Billy's fave is Wella Hard Rock Hairspray!) Mind you, there'd probably be an argument as to who was the more talented, good-looking and generally wondrous 'cos they're both in lurve with themselves!

MEL AND KIM AND THE PROCLAIMERS

Being sisters, Mel and Kim admit they're fairly close and a night out with Craig and Charlie Reid, alias The Proclaimers, would be, em, interesting, that's for sure. We reckon the Reid twins could do with a fun night out — they're a bit too old before their time for us. First they'd go for some scoff — to McDonalds or Wimpy — then it'd be on to the trendiest club of the moment to boogie away till the wee small hours. The girlies could teach the brothers how to groove, man, and teach them some funky dance routines — can you imagine The Proclaimers strutting their funky stuff — a fine 'spectacle', to be sure.

TINA TURNER AND DAVID BOWIE

Well, an obvious choice, we'd have thought. Neither Tina nor David are exactly your average spring chicken, but both still look great and are generally talented dudes, we'd say. Their perfect date? It'd have to be something fairly sophisticated for this cosmopolitan pair — they'd probably go to a Japanese restaurant for some sushi, then on to one of the posher clubs by limousine for a fun time of it. Yup, this trendy twosome can show many a young whippersnapper a thing or two.

BEN AND CAROL DECKER

Now, you may think this is a strange choice for a hot date, but there's a good reason for it. Ben is a mite pretentious, yah? Well, we reckon he'd be much nicer if he dropped his falseness and just acted naturally. So who better to show him just what a good time is than Carol Decker, t'lass with T'Pau? Yup, there's nowt phoney about this gal — all she's interested in is making a few good toons and having a laugh while she's at it. Whereas Ben talks about the meaning of life, how he suffers for his art, blah, blah, blah . . . tosh, in other words! Carol, get him down the disco for a wild night out and show him just what a good time is!

MATT DILLON AND SADE

Cool, sophisticated and a trifle mysterious — that's how both of these characters could be summed up. Not to mention extremely good-looking and talented, of course! Yup, we think Matt and Sade would get on just fine — and there'd be no attention-grabbing dates for this pair. No, a quiet meal à deux, then on to a funky, trendy jazz concert where they could groove the night away without many people annoying them. Aww . . .

THE ED AND A SCAREY PERSON

Ooh! Scarey! We may mock The Ed, but in real life we think she's great, ace, a toff. Well, we have to say that because she's such a scarey woman. She shouts! She screams! She throws things when our work is but a minute late! So she'd lurve a date with an equally scarey person — she'd go a bundle on a groovy night out with Ian Astbury, the Cult beast. We're sure he's a very nice man, in fact we like him, but let's face it, he looks fairly scarey all the same, so the two of them would have lots in common. Also, the pair have similar tastes in music, so a funky night out would be to go to a psychedelic disco, man, and get on down to many a hippy number while waving their love beads in the air and chanting their mantra-words.

Riding boots for cowgirls who like to stick the boot in.

Gold jewellery (real of course) — and lots of it!

C.D.'s: classical & contemporary.

Gloves — you've got to hand it to them — they're stylish.

Say 'style' with flowers.

Classy doctor's bag.

Loaf around stylishly!

Hip hip flask for hip chicks!

Slick

The Blue Jeans easy-to-follow guide to style. Get these and get groovy!

Cool Perrier for heated moments!

Smooth 'n' stylish Brylcreem for your man!

Love letters on Basildon Bond!

Clinique — hypo-allergenic make-up — luscious!

Heels — the classiest you can find!

Classic watch says it's time for style!

Filofax for stylish appointments!

Street sounds for street style.

Vidal 'slick' Sassoon mousse.

Belt up!

Get stuck in in Docs!

You can't do without a crisp white shirt.

BLUE JEANS
HUNK No.4
James Dean

Lisa Said...

It's easy to see now how stupid I was to listen to Lisa. But at the time, I was caught up in a fantasy world that had nothing to do with the way things really were . . .

I SHOULD never have listened to Lisa. But it's easy to say that now, when I can look back and see just how stupid I've been. At the time, I was flattered, excited, and naive enough to believe everything she said.

"Lee Russell fancies you," she told me.

That was the start of it.

Lee Russell was the best-looking boy I'd ever seen, the hero of every girl's dreams. I didn't know a single mate of mine who wouldn't have given her right arm for a chance of a night out with Lee Russell.

And, come to think of it now, that's all any of them had — just a night out with him. He wasn't the steady type. But perhaps that was the challenge, as far as I was concerned, anyway, because I was lumbered with a boy who was as steady as a rock, and about as exciting as one, too.

See, I said "lumbered". Because once Lisa started working on me that's how I started to think of Ray.

Ray wasn't everyone's idea of supermacho. He certainly wasn't Lisa's. Ever since I'd started going out with him, she'd been going on at me about how boring he was, and how he looked like Gordon the Gopher.

I liked him, though, a lot. I liked his quiet ways, and his unexpected jokes. I liked the way he cheered me up and really listened to me when I had something important to moan about or shout about. But Lisa said you didn't go out with a boy for that. She said that's what best friends were for, and that boyfriends were supposed to be romantic and sexy-looking, like Lee Russell.

"I've seen the way he keeps looking at you, Bev," she told me. "Honestly, if you didn't have Ray always hanging around, you'd be in with a real chance. You must've noticed the wink he gave you in Maths."

The idea of Lee Russell took hold of me, and started to grow. When I was with Ray, I started to see him the way Lisa saw him, not very good-looking, certainly not romantic, a mate, a kid to hang around with until something better showed up. And I couldn't help thinking, when Ray pecked my cheek and whispered, "See ya, sunshine!" at the end of another friendly evening together that it would be nice if he'd take me in his arms, slowly and gently, and kiss me in a way that would send the universe spinning. That would be how Lee Russell would kiss. Girls who'd been

out with him stayed in a state of dazed shock for two or three days at least!

"Of course, there's always Angie's party," Lisa grinned at me one day. "Isn't that on the night Ray's supposed to be going to London with his mum and dad? You could always . . ."

"Go to Angie's party without him?!" I finished the sentence for her.

"Well, what's the harm? He's going to London without you!" Lisa said.

"But that's to see his dad's cousin and . . ."

"Can't you take any chances, Bev? What do you see in him? Are you going to spend your life washing your hair on Saturday nights because your pet gopher isn't around?" she sneered.

I wanted to point out that it was only this Saturday night that he wouldn't be around. But I didn't. Because I thought, why not? Why not take the opportunity? Ray need never

know, and if it didn't work out between Lee and me, there was no harm done. But if it did . . . ? That was another question.

"Oh, and by the way," Lisa said, "Lee did happen to ask me, last night, if you'd be at Angie's party, and I did happen to mention that Ray was away for the evening, and that you might pop round, know what I mean?"

That settled it. I had to go to the party.

On the Friday night, Ray kept asking me what was wrong.

"If it's about tomorrow . . ." he said.

"No, it's not!" I snapped. But I was lying and I felt guilty.

"All I was going to say was that I'm sorry you won't be coming with us, but I'll try to call round, if we get back in time."

"Don't bother," I said, quickly. "I'd planned a nice quiet evening talking to the dog!"

"I'll see what I can manage," he said. But I wasn't really listening to him, or thinking about him. Only Angie's party mattered, and Lisa's latest bit of information.

"He said he'll see you there. Lee, I mean. He said he'll see you at the party."

All right, so it was stupid. But by Saturday night, I was totally caught up in this crazy scheme of Lisa's. I just wanted some other boy to dance with me, to pay some attention to me, to kiss me into a daze, and then, perhaps to say, "I'd like to see you again. You're the only girl who's ever really mattered to me, Bev!" The dream stopped there. It didn't include what I'd say to Ray, afterwards. Ray didn't count anymore.

LEE RUSSELL was at Angie's party. So was I. And Lisa, giggling, nudging me, pushed me in his direction. Not that I needed much pushing. Looking back now, I was fairly pathetic, all dressed up in my man-eating best, doing the eye-contact bit and the blushing and the secret smiles whenever he turned in my direction. It wasn't very often. Mostly, he was standing with the soccer mob, doing a minute-by-minute replay of that day's match in which he'd been the hero, as usual. But I tried harder, and in the end he sort of pulled me towards him and said, "What's your game, Bev? Thought you were going out with Ray Bramley?"

"Well, maybe I am, maybe I'm not," I answered, trying to make myself sound interesting.

"Make up your mind, kiddo," he grinned, "because right now he's standing over there, looking as if he's about to burst into tears!"

He ruffled my hair, and pulled me towards him, planting a kiss on my lips. It did nothing for me. In a way, it was just another show he was putting on, like his weekly goal-scoring. He wasn't even looking at me while he kissed me, but across at where Ray was standing in the doorway, next to Lisa.

I was just frozen. Yes, I let him kiss me, if you can call it kissing. But my eyes were staring at Ray's stricken face, at the eyes that gazed into mine with disbelief and hurt.

I broke away from Lee Russell's sweaty grip. He laughed, and returned to his mates. But when I reached the doorway, Ray had gone.

"He left. Best thing, too. How're you getting on with Lee? Looks as if you're making a big impression," Lisa said.

"Big impression?" I sobbed. "Come off it, Lisa. He's not interested in me. He never was. All he's interested in is himself!"

"So, OK, he's not quite the sensitive little soul that Ray is . . ." Lisa mumbled. "Listen, don't run after him, Bev. I'm going to see him tomorrow. I've said I'll call round and tell him how you feel. I'll do that for you."

"You'll . . . ?!" I screeched.

"Why not? What're friends for?" she asked.

It took a long time to sink in, for me to realise what Lisa had been doing all along, trying to split me and Ray up, because, right from the start, she'd fancied him herself. Lee Russell was just an idea she put into my head, so that she could take what she really wanted.

I know that now. Ray and I talked about it, and I think he understands, too. He never liked Lisa. But he's having problems forgiving me and trusting me. We're not going steady anymore. We're just talking, and it feels awkward, like two strangers. It's funny how you never realise what you want until you lose it. Perhaps there's hope for us again, some day, or perhaps it really is over. I'll keep working on it, and hoping, and regretting the day I let myself be flattered into doing something that ruined the best thing I ever had.

81

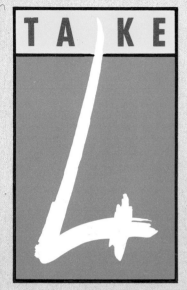

TAKE 4

FOUR LOOKS TO SAVE THE DAY AND GET YOU THROUGH IN STYLE . . .

SMART

Hat & brooch from
Top Shop.
Skirt, shirt & scarf
from Next.
Jacket from
Wrygges.
Tights & bag from
Chelsea Girl.
Shoes from
Saxone.

CASUAL

Shirt, belt, jumper
& boots from Next.
Tie & jeans from
Wrygges.

BED!

Pyjamas &
slippers from Top
Shop.
Toy dog from
Boots.

83

GLAM

Dress & bag from
Top Shop.
Gloves & jewellery
from Chelsea Girl.

ARE YOU SITTING COMFORTABLY?

No matter how you're feeling, there's a video to suit you every day of the year!

84

MUSICALS: Videos to Boogie On Down To!

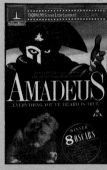

AMADEUS, Cert PG

Wot? Classical music — Eeeyurgh! Yup, that's what we thought, too, but in fact this video will make you see Mozart, Shostakovich, James Last and others 'of that ilk' (ooer!) in a different light. But especially Mozart, who as this film shows, was quite a little raver. This tale of the rise and decline of the Donny Osmond of his day will have you gripped to your seats as it's got a pretty sinister plot, too — woooo, spooky! And you'll emerge at the end of this movie positively yearning to hear more of that classical music stuff. Yessir!

GREASE, Cert PG

OK, OK, we *know* you've probably seen this movie a million, trillion times on TV but the fact remains that it's one of the best bopperoonies that the BJ Video Review Office knows. This is 'Love Story', Fifties style, and bloomin' exciting into the bargain! There's one stomping hit after another — and take our word for it, you'll LOVE to hate Olivia 'I'm so sickly sweet' Newts'n'toads.

STOP MAKING SENSE, Cert PG

Whether you're a Talking Heads fan or not, this is a visual experience in itself. Watching bands in concert can be pretty boring, it must be said — there's only so much rawkin' guitar-playing a gal can take. But with Talking Heads, the music is *almost* a subsidiary: marvel at David Byrne's infamous Big Suit! Gasp at the slide show backdrop! And exclaim loudly "Pheeeyooo!" at the whole band's seemingly non-stop energy. And we bet our bottom dollar that your foot'll be tappin' like a good 'un.

BLUE HAWAII, Cert PG

Actually, any Elvis Presley video would do just nicely. Currently undergoing something of a revival, Elvis was probably the first megastar to make rawkin' movies, and do it well. Here he plays Chad, an ex-G.I. who's finding his feet after coming out of the army. Problem is, he's got one plan for his life — and Mummy has a very different one. How do they sort it out? Well, Mum's the word (oh ha ha!) but you can bet that if there's an opportunity for a wee toon along the way, Pelvis Presley'll grab it!

SCARIES 'N' SPOOKIES

Have a cushion at the ready to cover your eyes from this little lot!

YOUNG SHERLOCK HOLMES AND THE PYRAMID OF FEAR, Cert PG

A birrovacorny idea, this is — ol' Sherlock-baby is in fact scarcely out of his romper suits at this stage, but still manages to solve a dastardly crime or two. He meets up with Watson, a newcomer to his school, and the pair of them (plus, of course, Holmes' amazing powers of observation) attempt to find a link between a series of mysterious 'suicides'. A fearsome little film, this turns out to be, with lashings of death, disaster and dastardly fiends!

LITTLE SHOP OF HORRORS, Cert PG

GHOSTBUSTERS, Cert PG

OK, OK, we're cheatin' here, admittedly, but these two combine spooky scarey plots with a lorra lorra laughs. In 'Little Shop Of Horrors', a weird and wonderful plant has a very dodgy food supply which is warm and red and sticky and inside human bodies. (Have you guessed what it is yet?) But the fun with this one is — it's a musical! So you can singalongamurderers — hurrah!

There're lots of spooks a-floatin' around in 'Ghostbusters' — but not for long, once the Ghostbuster team get swatting them. The special effects on both vids'll have you cowering behind the settee.

THE HUNCHBACK OF NOTRE DAME, Cert PG

"The bells! The bells!" Another classic movie from days gone by,

SMOOCHIES: Some happy tales of lurve and stuff!

MANNEQUIN, Cert PG

Johnathan Switcher has an embarrassing problem. He's fallen in love with a bit of wood! A piece of wood which stands naked in shop windows! A mannequin, to be precise, which comes alive when no one else is looking! Yup, incredible, innit? But he's no dummy, is Johnathan (hahahahaha) and persists in his lurve despite everything. Who said what an idiot?! Acksherly, this is a jolly good kissy kissy movie. And Andrew McCarthy's in it.

ANNIE HALL, Cert 15

This is subtitled 'a nervou romance', and if Woody Allen's g anything to do with it (which he mo: certainly has), there'll be lots and lot of nerves and a smidgeon of romanc The film's got a nice warm glow to 'cos it's the story of two people wh fall in love — with all the litt pleasures and pitfalls that entails – it's full of gentle humour and, as yo can probably tell, a winner for u Need we say more?

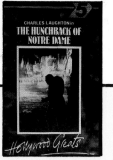

...arles Laughton (ask your ...nies...) plays a blubbering ...ck of a hunchback who falls ...elessly in lurve with beautiful ...sy wench, Maureen O'Hara and the ...le thing comes to a somewhat — ...sticky end... But our Charlie's ...retty ugly and scarey character ...way, so who cares? (Oh, so crool! ...utting!)

...DIANA JONES AND THE ...MPLE OF DOOM, Cert PG

...Any excuse to include Harrison ...d in the proceedings! The sequel to ...iders Of The Lost Ark', this film has ...y searching for the v.v.v. precious ...ara Stone and endeavouring to ...rieve thousands of children ...laved by a mysterious cult. Much ...shing of swords, creeping of crawly ...ngs, and generally being ...oetually on the edge of disaster. ...the mere glimpse of Harry's ...ling biceps can work wonders in ...king you forget the scarey bits! All ...ll, it's a riveting little number.

...RETTY IN PINK, Cert 15

...A Brat Pack special! Molly ...igwald plays Andie Walsh who's ...dly in love with rich preppie, Blane. ...d he fancies her, too. Hurrah! ...cept... they come from such ...ferent backgrounds that there's ...und to be problems. And there are. ...s isn't helped by the fact that ...cky Dale, crazy character ...raordinaire, is madly in love with ...die, too. Or by the fact that Andie's ...opa is a rampaging alcoholic. ...nfused? You won't be — it's really ...tty simple, you see Andie Walsh... ...never mind, in any case she's in a ...sition we'd all love to be in, ...oosing between Jon Cryer and ...drew McCarthy. One of the bestest ...at Pack videos around, and a real ...sy cuddly one!

FUNNIES: If you're in the mood for a giggle, these'll have you in stitches!

CROCODILE DUNDEE, Cert 15

Top of the film and video top tens for many months, it won't take you long to realise why it's such a smash. Fresh from advertising a certain Australian lager, Paul Hogan, the cuddliest Aussie since Skippy the Bush Kangaroo (who?) comes bouncing on to your screens.

Michael J. 'Crocodile' Dundee, a brash, big-mouthed and burly bloke, has survived months in the Australian outback: now can he survive a week in New York? He does — but there's many mistakes and blunders to be made on the way, and ol' Paul makes them with style! Turn a blind eye if you can to the foxlicious Linda Kozlowski who plays his journalist "friend". 'Cos she'll make you think twice about eating that third Wispa — and who'd want that??

¡THREE AMIGOS!, Cert PG

As far as the video review office is concerned, you only have to cast a glance at Steve Martin and you're rolling in the aisles. Here, he teams up with Chevy Chase and Martin Short, to play three out-of-luck silent screen actors, who, when fired by the studio, end up saving a small Mexican village from a gang of extremely not-very-nice and dastardly banditos. Even the actors' names are hilarious — Lucky Day, Dusty Bottoms and Ned Nederlander. And with cactus galore into the bargain the whole thing's a larf and a half!

AIRPLANE!, Cert PG

Just when you thought it was safe to go winging off to Majorca, this'll have you checking up the bus times, to be sure! When the crew of an airliner comes down with food poisoning, the only person able to save the passengers happens to be an ex-fighter pilot with an intense fear of flying. That's v.v. serious-sounding, but when nearly every scene's a rip off of—well, just about everything you *can* rip-off—there's nary a dull moment. A hilarity hit!

STIR CRAZY, Cert 15

A case of poor boys making good, this is — or at least, trying to! More out-of-work actors, here, but this time they try their luck promoting a bank dressed up as woodpeckers. Yes, woodpeckers! While they're on their tea-break, some dastardly fiends steal their cozzies and commit a fiendish robbery on the bank. And guess who ends up in jail? Yup, Gene Wilder and Richard Pryor, the pretty darned unlucky actors. So they very sensibly stage an escape, and they stir things up extremely crazily in the process...

85

WEEPIES: If you're feeling blue, these *aren't* for you!

BRIEF ENCOUNTER, Cert PG

BJ's personal fave, and proof that the Oldies are the v.v.v. Goodies! Two people are thrown together by fate — a chance meeting in a BR buffet bar, to be precise — and fall helplessly in love. But it's hopeless — 'cos they're both married (to other people, you clot!) and the affair must end, sniff! But we're telling you the plot!! Git on down and suss out this vid, it'll have you reaching for the Kleenex.

TEARMS OF ENDEARMENT, Cert PG

If you think *you've* got problems with your mother, you should see the poor girlie in this video! Talk about 'stormy relationship'! A star studded cast (Jack "Sneersome" Nicholson, Debra "Foxsome" Winger) keeps things snappy, and you'll be in stitches for the most part. But there's a wailsome twist in the tale that accounts for 'Terms of Endearment's' reputation as one of the great modern-day weepies.

GONE WITH THE WIND, Cert PG

From a modern day weepie to a classic one... Ask your mums and aunties about Clark Gable and without a doubt their eyes'll go all glazed and they'll get a faraway dreamy look... for Clark Gable is the original Bit Of Stuff! So let this epic carry you back to the days gone by when beautiful women had not a care in the world but for the latest fashion fripperies — oh, except for the American Civil War, which, if you happened to be in the States, was probably a bit of a bummer. Scarlett O'Hara copes admirably — but she does have plenty of love interest to keep her going. Check out this one — and be prepared to weep buckets!

NO PROBLEM!

Don't let flaking nails or clogged mascara get you down — watch this space for the answers to all your beauty problems . . .

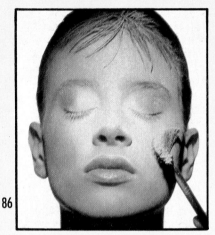

86

Q I like wearing foundation, as it hides all the various blemishes and freckles on my face. The only trouble is, I don't seem to be able to apply it without leaving streaks. What's the correct way to apply foundation?
Amy, Gwent.

A If you find it difficult to apply this without leaving streaks, use a translucent foundation — that way the streaks will be less noticeable if you do have them!
The best way to apply foundation though, is to use a damp cosmetic sponge. Try to buy one that's wedge-shaped so you can get at all those difficult areas around your face!
After you've cleansed, toned and moisturised your face, dot the foundation over small areas at a time and smooth it over the skin with the damp sponge. Use small amounts of foundation so that your skin doesn't look clogged. Use the thin end of the sponge to smooth foundation up to the hairline and around the eye area. Don't leave a line of it across your jaw — blend down on to the neck using the sponge. To set your foundation apply a dusting of translucent face powder.

Q I have never changed the colour of my hair, but I'm getting a bit bored with the same old mousey-brown shade. I don't want to buy a permanent hair colour in case I don't like the end result. What other forms of hair colour are available?
Alison, London.

A A semi-permanent colour is ideal for those who want to make their hair look a little more exciting. It will wash out after several shampoos, so it's good if you're just experimenting with colour.
If you want to lighten your hair, however, you'll have to go for a permanent tint.
This doesn't have to be an all over colour though, as your hairdresser can give you highlights in several different shades which can give your hair the overall effect of being lighter.
Fine highlights are what you should go for if you don't want your dark roots to show when they grow out. All you need to do is to have regular trims which will keep your hair in good condition and shape.
For wash-out colour, try out the Alberto VO5 range of tinted mousses.

Q I don't know which is the best method of removing unwanted hair for me, as depilatory creams usually irritate my skin, and I don't like the rough stubble that shaving leaves. What would you suggest I use to remove hair from my legs?
Karen, Devon.

A To avoid the problems you have experienced with depilatory creams and shaving, try waxing your legs.
You can buy leg waxing kits inexpensively at most chemists. Avoid the type of wax which you have to heat up before applying, as it's all too easy to burn yourself! Go instead for the cold sticky wax strips which you simply apply and strip off.
Waxing can be a bit nippy at first, but it is a very efficient way of removing hair right down to the roots. You shouldn't see any regrowth for at least three weeks.

Q Although my teeth are healthy and nicely shaped, they let me down because they're so yellow. What can I do to make them whiter?
Sara, Nottingham.

A Drinking too much coffee, tea or cola can make your teeth yellow, as can smoking. Specially formulated preparations are available on the market for whitening teeth, but should not be used too often.
Try out this tooth preparation which you can make yourself at home: — Mix 3 tablespoons of bicarbonate of soda with 2 tablespoons of salt. Keep it in a jar and just dip your toothbrush into it before cleaning your teeth. The mixture really whitens teeth, and keeps them looking healthy.

Q My eyeshadow never stays put, it always seems to crease after a couple of hours. What kind of eyeshadow should I use for a long-lasting effect?
Pam, Oxford.

A The creasing of eyeshadow can be caused by either applying it when your eyelids have a little grease on them, or by using a cream shadow when you are usually prone to oily skin.
Before applying your eyeshadow, make sure all traces of cleanser have been removed with a damp cotton-wool ball. Dust your eyelids with loose translucent face powder before applying your eyeshadow. If you have oily skin, use a powder shadow rather than a creamy one and avoid soft eye pencils, which will also smudge easily.

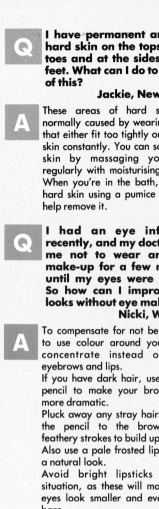

Q I have permanent areas of hard skin on the tops of my toes and at the sides of my feet. What can I do to get rid of this?

Jackie, Newcastle.

A These areas of hard skin are normally caused by wearing shoes that either fit too tightly or rub the skin constantly. You can soften the skin by massaging your feet regularly with moisturising cream. When you're in the bath, rub the hard skin using a pumice stone to help remove it.

Q I had an eye infection recently, and my doctor told me not to wear any eye make-up for a few months until my eyes were better. So how can I improve my looks without eye make-up?

Nicki, Walsall.

A To compensate for not being able to use colour around your eyes, concentrate instead on your eyebrows and lips.
If you have dark hair, use a dark pencil to make your brows look more dramatic.
Pluck away any stray hairs, apply the pencil to the brows using feathery strokes to build up colour. Also use a pale frosted lipstick for a natural look.
Avoid bright lipsticks in this situation, as these will make your eyes look smaller and even more bare.

Q I use foundation all the time to try and hide the open pores on my nose, but they're still really obvious. Is there anything I can do to close them up a bit?

Lesley, Glasgow.

A Open pores are common amongst people with oily skin. Instead of using foundation all the time, which will probably block your pores, use a toner after cleansing. Regular use of this will help to close the pores, as will the weekly use of a face mask specially formulated for oily skin.

Q No matter how much I try to condition my hair, it's still dull and lifeless and won't sit in any sort of style. What can I do?

Lisa, Hull.

A Hair can often become dull and floppy when excess amounts of shampoo and conditioner are used and not rinsed out properly. Try pepping up your mop with a vinegar rinse. OK — it may leave you smelling a little dodgy, but it will work wonders on your hair!
Mix ½ a cup of vinegar and ½ a cup of water. After shampooing and conditioning, apply this mixture to your hair before giving it a final rinse with cool water.
You can give your hair a lift by applying a firm hold mousse, making sure you comb it through from roots to tips. When styling your hair, direct hot jets of air from hairdryer at the hair roots. Holding your head upside down when drying the hair will also give your style a lift.

Q My nails always start to flake when I try to grow them. They seem to be really weak. How can I strengthen them?

Annie, Liverpool.

A Your nails are probably too dry, so you should regularly massage a nourishing nail cream into the base of your nails. Keep them fairly short to begin with, and use a nail hardener. Never use a metal nail file, only emery boards. Try to eat a balanced diet consisting of

enough meat, eggs, fish, fruit and vegetables. This will keep your nails (as well as the rest of you!) in good condition.

Q My mascara always seems to become clogged, making my eyelashes stick together. The rest of my make-up usually looks OK, but the lumpy mascara spoils the whole look. Is there anything I can do?

Wendy, Surrey.

A Use an old toothbrush, or invest in an eyelash comb to separate your lashes and remove lumps of mascara just after you've applied it. The older your mascara is, the more likely it is to be dry and lumpy. Replace it every few months with a new tube.

Q I have thin lips, but when I wear lipstick, they look practically non-existent. How can I make them look bigger?

Val, Manchester.

A Firstly, you should avoid dark lipsticks, as these will make your lips "disappear".
You could try using lipliner outside your natural lip line then filling in with lipstick, but this means you do have to keep checking that it hasn't smudged. Alternatively, outline your natural lip line with a fairly pale lip liner, then fill in with a slightly darker, toning lipstick. Use soft natural colours which won't attract attention to your lips.

87

SEXY

'Men' are subjects which are never very far from the normal thinking girl's mind. And why not? A healthy moderate obsession never did anyone any harm after all! But what exactly is so appealing about 'the opposite sex'? What is that certain charm they have over us by which we are held spellbound and which causes our hearts to pound whenever they're in our presence? When we see a guy in the street, disco, house-party etc. and don't pass him off as a spotty wimp, but actually look twice, we know there's some sort of attraction there. But *what* sort of attraction exactly? We're attracted to men in many different ways usually reflected in our vivid descriptions of their personage: common examples include:—

"Corr! Worra hunk."

"He's wonderful — he's totally loaded."

"Look at that body."

"He's *such* a nice guy."

"He's OK, but I wouldn't mind his friend."

"Aah — those eyes!"

All indications of why we fancy a guy. Sometimes it's because he's nice looking or has a nice personality or has a nice car or even just because he's got a 'nice' group of friends. But it's always because he's 'sexy'.

Few relationships can survive on the grounds of one partner's wealth, personality or just good looks, a mutual infatuation and respect is the over-riding factor in most well-known, long-lasting twosomes.

A sexy guy in one girl's eyes may be a fat, ugly plonker in another's; this emotion is entirely personal.

88

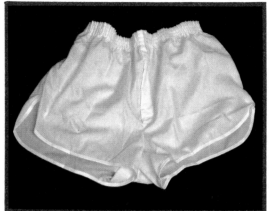
Even Bernard Manning in boxers is sexy! (Are you feeling OK? — The Ed.)

Sophia Loren — nice face, shame about the hair!

Nastassja Kinski — Oh well, us mere mortals can but dream!

Bryan Ferry — even sexier than the flower pot!

SEXY WOMEN

Sade	Catherine
Sophia Loren	Deneuve
Marilyn Monroe	Chrissie Hynde
Beatrice Dalle	Lisa Bonet
Annie Lennox	Elizabeth Taylor
Kim Basinger	(in her early days)
Debbie Harry	Vivien Leigh
Patsy Kensit	
Meryl Streep	
Nastassja Kinski	

IS...

Timothy Dalton — very sexy whether shaken or stirred!

Corr! Worra dish!

SEXY IS . . .

Antaeus
Shirt and tie
White T-shirt
Clean shaven men
Golf GTI Convertible
501's ripped at the bum
Armani suits
Chanel No. 5
Obsession
Foreign accents
Big ears
Chocolate mousse
Natural tans
Shoulders
Sunday mornings
Pyjama bottoms
Older men
White notepaper
'The Independent'
Husky voices
Black

89

SEXY MEN

Morrissey
Bob Geldof
Mickey Rourke
Barry Kamen
Michael Brandon
Count Dracula from
Sesame St.
The blond in the
'Start' ad.

Frank Sinatra
Cary Grant
James Dean
Montgomery Clift
Matt Dillon
Marlon Brando
Bryan Ferry
Timothy Dalton
Rupert Everett
Sean Connery
Billy Idol

T'Pau CD — smooch sexily to the groove!

The ultimate! Sexy black stockings.

Sean Connery — sexier than his son and that's saying something!

Chanel Antaeus— The mark of a real man.

....SEXY

NOT SO SEXY MEN
Nik Kershaw
The Proclaimers
Phil Collins
Zodiac Mindwarp
Shane MacGowan
Gary Moore
Jonathan King
Keith Chegwin
Tony Blackburn
Jeff Banks
Nick Kamen
Jonathan Woss
Steve Walsh
Rick Astley
Bernard Manning
Beastie Boys
Paul Daniels
Slade

How much sex-appeal has this man got? Not a lot!

No, Marilyn, don't even bother trying!

90

FABERGÉ

BRUT
FOR MEN

SPRAY LOTION

Brut 33—
The mark of
a real prat!

American Tan tights.
— Mmm!

How about a pair of kinky,
manly red Y's for your
No 1 hunk? Maybe not!

About as much
sex-appeal as bile!

ISN'T?

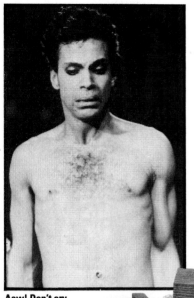

Aaw! Don't cry, Prince, you can't help having the ugliest belly-button in pop.

SEXY ISN'T

Sticky-out belly buttons
Pork scratchings
Trainers
Clapped out Cortinas
Skin-tight jeans
Concept Man suits
Horny toe nails
Goatee beards
Greying underwear
Yellow Y-fronts

Brut 33
Limara
Tweed
Smoking
Big bellies
Garlic
Warts
The Sun
Socks in bed
Brown
Swearing

You'd have to be blind to date lurverly Cilla.

91

Tweed perfume—
B.O.'s better any day!

NOT SO SEXY WOMEN

Whitney Houston
Fatima Whitbread
Dee Hepburn
Lulu
Mandy Smith
Anita Dobson
Bananarama
Cilla Black
Marti Kane
Tina Turner
Selina Scott
Kim Wilde
Marilyn
Fuzz-Box
Sam Fox
Muriel Gray
Madonna

Cor! 'Ave a butcher's at this ol' paper bag. Almost as sexy as Effel's little Willie!

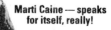

Madonna CD — for passion killers everywhere.

Marti Caine — speaks for itself, really!

Sweet Dreams...

Strange things can happen in your dreams, like running up the High Street naked or eating mountains of Big Macs — but should we take any notice of them?

ALTHOUGH dreams have been studied for thousands of years, they're still a mystery to us all!

Everyone dreams, and very often what happens in our dreams can be as strange as science fiction, so funny we wake ourselves laughing, or as sad as the weepiest film imaginable.

Most dreams take place in the minutes when we're dropping off to sleep, or during the few minutes it takes us to wake up from a deep snooze. It's said they only last for a few seconds, even although they seem to go on for a lot longer than that!

You may find that you share the same types of dreams with other people.

A common recurring dream is one where you feel that you're falling from a great height, and just before you hit the ground, you wake up with a jolt.

Another is when you're trying to get somewhere in a hurry, or you're being chased, and you can't seem to run quickly enough. Your legs feel as if they're moving under water!

Many people also dream that they're in a car with someone, when the person who's driving suddenly slumps in the seat, and the dreamer has to try and drive the car before it crashes!

Sounds familiar, eh?!!

As the boys and girlies at BJ have had so many weird and wonderful dreams, we decided to jot a few of them down, along with their meanings . . . man!

JANE

I once dreamt I was at a party and I was having a great time — the only odd thing about the party was that all the guests were penguins!

● Dreaming of birds usually means that if you're poor and struggling, there will be an improvement in your cash flow situation. It's also a good omen to dream about being at a party, but only if you're enjoying yourself and it's not your party!

ALI

I often dream that I'm in a swimming pool which only has about two inches of water in it. Under that, there's broken glass and I have to drag myself along it to get out. Just to make things a little more complicated, I'm usually in a race with about ten other people who're swimming away quite happily!

● This weird dream really sounds as if something nasty is going to happen, but if you dream about swimming in a pool, it means you'll be successful! Swimming to reach your objective means that you'll have success in everything because you're willing to work hard. Because there was broken glass under the water, it's probably a sign that you're more determined than most in what you do! *(Where's that pay rise? —Ali.)*

A date with Rod Stewart was my weirdest dream — maybe it should be classed as a nightmare! I dreamt he took me out for a meal — quite a horrifying thought considering he has the same effect on me as eating two dozen Wispas one after the other. Why couldn't it have been Terence Trent D'Arby who'd asked me out?

● It may seem strange that in your dream you were out with someone you don't like normally, but dreams concerning meals usually mean the opposite of what they seem. So don't worry — you don't have a secret yearning for old Rod!

Dates in dreams mean that you're admired by a member of the opposite sex. Lucky you!

When I was younger, I used to dream I was one of the Caped Crusaders and I could fly. I'd only have to run and jump with my arms in the air, and I'd take off like a rocket. The only problem was that quite often I'd be chased by a giant and my flying powers would fail. The result was that I'd be running as fast as I could taking little jumps every so often!

● This probably means that you're perhaps being a little too ambitious for your own good! You're more than likely trying to carry out too many plans that you don't really have time for.

Oddly enough, if you dream about giants, it means you'll probably overcome your difficulties if you face them boldly.

JACQUIE

I had quite a vivid dream about me and Billy Idol once, but enough said about that! I have lots of weird dreams and I often dream about falling off things. I wake up in a cold sweat with my heart thumping! Does this mean I'm maybe a bit strange?!!
● Yes, well, we all know you're strange, Jacquie . . . hate to say this, but falling from a height is a sign of bad luck, and the further you fall, the worse your luck will be! If you fall without being injured though, it means you will win any fights you have!

LESLEY

I once dreamt that I was slurping head first down a water chute which was full of Noodle-Doodles. I had to eat loads of them on my way down, and the tomato sauce was beginning to make me sick! (Noodle-Doodles, for all those who're interested, are pasta shapes in tomato sauce.)
● It's usually a good sign to eat food in your dreams, as long as you're soon full up. If you stuff your face in your dream though, it means bad luck's on the way! If you're vomiting in your dream it means that money is winging its way to you, but only if you're poor at that time.

MORAG

My dreams quite often consist of mad people chasing me around the house while I'm frantically trying to lock doors to keep them out. Sometimes I can't actually see who's chasing me. Weird, eh?
● Dreaming about mad people often indicates that you want to do well for yourself and make plenty of money! Running because you're afraid means that you have a fear of being rejected by friends.

VAL

Sometimes I dream that I'm trying to get to an important meeting or place but things keep happening to slow me down. Then at last I arrive, look down and realise I've come out with my slippers on!
● If you dream of going out when you're not properly dressed, you should be careful in what you say and do. It also means that gossip worries you. Being without shoes though, is a really lucky sign for you — you'll be successful in business!

YVONNE

I once dreamt I was walking down a busy street when a man came charging along the road in something like an old-fashioned stagecoach. He was standing on top of it, lunging at everyone with a huge syringe. He got me in the leg with it and it was really painful. When I woke up, I had a big scratch down my leg . . . spook!
● To dream that you have pain in your leg means that you'll soon be receiving good news! As you were pricked with a syringe it could be classed as a vaccination, in which case you're in danger of being too affectionate to someone who doesn't deserve it.
    If, in your dream, you're in a crowd, it means you'll go far!

As you've probably had many a strange dream that you'd like to interpret, here's a list of dreams topics and what they mean!

● Apart from a few exceptions, many meanings of dreams are exactly the opposite of what they seem to be. For instance, dreaming of death means a marriage or happiness, a struggle means great improvements are being made, and dreams of murder means safety.
● Wild cats and large animals in your dreams is a sign of bad luck.
● All pets (apart from cats) in your dreams mean good luck.
● Fish mean wealth is coming your way, especially if they're floating on the surface of the water.
● If you dream of drifting upwards, you're going to be very lucky!
● Beware if you dream of vegetables! Don't panic however if your dreams include mushrooms or peas as they indicate money and success!
● Dreaming of a picnic means there's doubt concerning a love affair!
● Greenfly, spiders, flies and all sorts of other house and garden creepy-crawlies in your dreams mean that you'll do better in life than you ever dreamed you would!
● If you're sneezing because you've had a whiff of some pepper in your dream, it means there's talent in your family.

93

Cilla Black (1)

Well, she seems to have improved with age! Of course, it's old Cilla Black, that sincere little celebrity we know and love so well. She looks as if that same suit has made a trip to the tailors and been restyled. With the money she's raking in?! The BJ gang decree that she should start investing in some rawk 'n' roll togs now!

94

Michael Jackson (4)

OK, you can open your eyes again. That ghastly bolero jacket has gone! In its place is a rather "fetching" space suit come pullover, sported by none other than Michael Jackson. Forget the clothes for a minute, will you just check out what this man has done to his face? If that nose got any thinner it would disappear altogether! He seems to have got a lot paler too, but perhaps that's the shock of selling all those squillions of groovy discs. This man probably funds the whole of the American plastic surgery business single handed!

Tina Turner (2)

My, my, what hairdressers can do nowadays! That horror of the front pages is actually Tina Turner! Obviously turning to vegetarianism and a touch of the spooky old Bhuddist chanting has done her a power of good. Perhaps the only woman in the world who looks better with a frizzy moppish hairstyle rather than her own natural "tresses". Yup, we've got to hand it to old Tina, she sure is a foxtress, if even a middle-aged one!

David Cassidy (3)

Of course! It's David Cassidy, and no doubt about it — his hairstyle may have improved somewhat but it's still obvious he should shoot his tailor! Thankfully David's true fans are now "getting on a bit" and can't sprint after him as speedily as they once did. If it came to a fast getaway, poor David's legs would be in severe danger of massive friction burns from those one squillion percent genuine nylon trousers.